U0064794

背「英文一字金」讓我心驚膽寒

　　在我的高中同學中，品德不好、喜歡抽煙、調皮搗蛋、打麻將、走極端的人，現在不是窮困潦倒，就是已經過世。我們首先要教導自己和孩子，做一個好人。每天背「英文一字金③金玉良言經」，背多了，自然受到影響。如：

Don't be evil.（不要做壞人。）
Don't be vicious.（不要有壞心眼。）
Don't be wicked.（不要當壞人。）

Don't be foul.（不要讓人討厭。）
Don't be rotten.（不要做爛人。）
Don't be violent.（不要有暴力傾向。）

如果什麼事都隱藏在心中，不說出來，讓人捉摸不定，結果吃虧的是自己。我哥哥八十多歲，存了一筆錢，想要幫助他的小孩買房子，但是他的孩子，打死不說自己每個月有多少收入，有多少存款，學美國人，說這是隱私，結果吃了大虧，我哥哥有錢沒地方送，只能留給孫子。所以，我們在「金玉良言經」中，勸別人：

Don't conceal.（不要隱瞞。）
Don't be vague.（不要說話模糊。）
Don't be obscure.（不要讓人難以了解。）

Don't puzzle.（不要使人困惑。）
Don't pretend.（不要作假。）
Don't be dishonest.（不要不誠實。）

不管小孩或大人，有話直說，不要隱瞞，別人才會接受你。

罵人，最受傷害的是自己。背完「金玉良言經」後，我就不敢再罵人了。笑臉迎人，福自天來。

　　Don't scold.（不要責罵人。）
　　Don't condemn.（不要罵人。）
　　Don't degrade others.（不要貶低別人。）

　　Don't blame others.（不要責備別人。）
　　Don't swear.（不要罵髒話。）
　　Don't curse.（不要罵髒話。）

　　Don't judge.（不要批評。）
　　Don't criticize.（不要批評。）
　　Don't be critical.（不要愛批評。）

一定要隨時隨地控制自己的情緒。*Don't be emotional.*（不要情緒化。）生氣的時候，最好離開現場，不要見不喜歡的人。

「金玉良言經」中，讓我最受益的一句話是：*Don't argue.*（不要爭論。）解決了我不少的煩惱。內人心地很好，但她有事沒事就會講一些刺激我的話。背了「英文一字金」後，我會轉移話題，不爭論，用英文對她說：

Don't start conflict.（不要先引起衝突。）
Don't be contrary.（不要為了反對而反對。）
Don't be contradictory.（不要老是唱反調。）

她每天聽我背「英文一字金」，現在已經開始背「金玉良言經」了，性格變得非常體貼、溫柔，我們的夫妻關係越來越好。

劉毅

背「一字金」是在使用英文

背了「金玉良言經」（Good Advice: What Not to Do），心驚膽寒，很多事情一輩子不能做，如 *Don't argue.*（不要爭論。）天天背，自然就受到影響，從此不再跟人爭論。美國有名的作家 Dale Carnegie 說："The only way to get the best of an argument is to avoid it."（要從爭論中獲益，唯一的方法就是避免爭論。）*Don't argue.* 這兩個字不知道能解決你多少煩惱。

一個字一句話，簡潔有力，像 *Don't assume.*（不要自以為是。）(= *Don't assume you're always right.*) 背「英文一字金」，不只是學英文，而是在使用英文。當別人跟你爭吵時，你可以跟他說：*Don't start conflict.*（不要先引起衝突。）*Don't conceal.*（不要隱瞞。）這句話教導我，有話直說，不隱瞞任何事，心情會變得很愉快。從 *Don't curse.* 和 *Don't swear.* 學到，不要用髒話罵人。背了「金玉良言經」，當你勸導別人時，更是警惕自己。

一般人喜歡抱怨，傷害自己，也傷害別人，你天天背：*Don't complain.*（不要抱怨。）自然受到影響。*Don't complicate.* 這句話教導我們，不要把事情複雜化，什麼都要簡化。英文一定要使用才不會忘記，如 choke（噎住）這個字，可引申為「出錯」。看到朋友緊張的時候，你可以跟他說：*Don't choke.*（不要驚慌出錯。）falter 這個字的主要意思是「搖晃」，你即使背了下來，也不會用，但美國人常說：*Don't falter.*（不要猶豫。）(= *Don't hesitate.*) 如果你只背 choke 和 falter 而不會用，遲早會忘記。

有些難背的單字，可以用「英文一字金」的方法，一次背好。如 dramatic、dreadful、dreary，這三個字都是 dr 開頭，馬上就可以背下來。你看到一個人很激動，你就可以說：***Don't be dramatic.***（不要太激動。）如果你只背單字，dramatic 是「戲劇性的」，就永遠不會用。

用「英文一字金」，說出來的話，人人佩服你，因為你所說的話是有程度的。

一 般 語 言	英 文 一 字 金
Don't just argue. Don't always disagree. （不要老是反對。）	***Don't be contradictory.*** ***Don't be contrary.*** （不要唱反調。不要為反對而反對。）
Don't be sad. （不要傷心。）	***Don't grieve.*** （不要傷心。）
Don't hesitate. （不要猶豫。）	***Don't falter.*** （不要猶豫。）
Don't make a mistake. （不要犯錯。）	***Don't choke.*** （不要驚慌出錯。）
Don't be angry. （不要生氣。）	***Don't be defensive.***（不要被激怒。） ***Don't be dramatic.***（不要太激動。）

一般人學英語會話，東學一點、西學一點，學的東西不確實，沒有成就感。用「英文一字金」來學，A 學完學 B，B 學完學 C，一本一本地學，自己可以感覺到，英文實力快速地增加，每天都學到東西，每天有成就感，快樂無比。

劉毅

Good Advice: What Not to Do

1. A

看英文唸出中文	一口氣 説 九 句	看中文唸出英文
abandon[4] 〔 ə'bændən 〕*v.*	字首 是 ab {	Don't *abandon* others. 不要拋棄別人。	拋棄
abuse[6] 〔 ə'bjuz 〕*v.*		*Abuse* anyone. 不要虐待任何人。	虐待
ambush[6] 〔'æmbuʃ 〕*v.*		*Ambush*. 不要暗算別人。	埋伏
argue[2] 〔'ɑrgju 〕*v.*		*Argue*. 不要爭論。	爭論
assault[5] 〔 ə'sɔlt 〕*v. n.*	字首 是 Ass {	*Assault*. 不要攻擊別人。	攻擊
assume[4] 〔 ə's(j)um 〕*v.*		*Assume*. 不要自以為是。	假定； 認為
annoy[4] 〔 ə'nɔɪ 〕*v.*		*Annoy*. 不要使人心煩。	使心煩
alienate[6] 〔'eljən‚et 〕*v.*		*Alienate*. 不要排擠 別人，使自己孤立。	使疏遠
average[3] 〔'ævərɪdʒ 〕*adj.*		Be *average*. 不要不上不下。	平均的

A

I. 背景説明：

Don't abandon others. 可説成：*Don't abandon* a friend in trouble.（不要拋棄在困難中的朋友。）美國人常會對朋友開玩笑説：*Don't abandon* me.（不要拋棄我。）還可勸告別人：*Don't abandon* your goals.（不要放棄你的目標。）*Don't abandon* your morals.（不要放棄你的道德標準。）*Abuse anyone.* 在此源自：Don't *abuse anyone.*（不要虐待任何人。）Don't *abuse* yourself.（不要虐待自己。）abuse 還可作「濫用」解。Don't *abuse* your authority.（不要濫用你的權威。）*Ambush.* 在此指 Don't *ambush* others.（不要暗算別人。）朋友之間最忌諱背叛。Don't be a back-stabber.（不要在人背後捅一刀。）(= *Don't be a rat.*)

Argue. 在此等於 Don't *argue.*（不要爭論。）可説成：Don't *argue* with others.（不要和別人爭論。）Don't waste time *arguing.*（不要浪費時間爭論。）*Arguing* gets you nowhere.（爭論沒有好處。）(= *Arguing doesn't improve a situation.*) *Assault.* 在此等於 Don't *assault* others.（不要攻擊別人。）Don't let yourself be *assaulted.*（不要讓自己被攻擊。）*Assume.* 在此等於 Don't *assume* anything.（不要什麼都自以為是。）Don't *assume* people are on your side.（不要認為人們在你那一邊。）Don't *assume* you're always right.（不要認為你一定是對的。）

Annoy. 在這裡是指 Don't *annoy* people.（不要使人心煩。）Don't *annoy* your friends.（不要使你的朋友心煩。）Don't let anything *annoy* you.（不要讓任何事情使你心煩。）*Alienate.* 在此是指 Don't *alienate* others.（不要排擠別人。）(= *Don't separate someone on purpose.*) Don't *alienate* yourself from society.（不要使自己與社會疏遠。）(= *Don't separate yourself from people.*) Don't *alienate* potential supporters.（不要疏遠潛在的支持者。）背 alienate，可先背 alien（外星人），因為外星人離我們很遠。*Be average.* 在此指 Don't *be average.*（不要做一般人。）Be an above *average* person.（要比一般人好。）(= *Be better than average.*)

II. 英語演講：

【一字英語演講】

Hey, I've got some advice for you!

Don't abandon others.

Abuse anyone.

Ambush.

Argue.

Assault.

Assume.

Annoy.

Alienate.

Be average.

Trust me. This is good advice.

【短篇英語演講】

Hey, I've got some advice for you!
嘿，我一些建議要給你們！

Don't abandon others. 不要拋棄別人。
Don't *abuse anyone.* 不要虐待任何人。
Don't *ambush* people. 不要暗算別人。

Don't waste time *arguing*. 不要浪費時間爭論。
Don't let yourself be *assaulted*.
不要讓自己被攻擊。
Don't *assume* anything. 不要什麼都自以為是。

Don't *annoy* people. 不要使人心煩。
Don't *alienate* others. 不要離間別人。
Don't *be* an *average* person. 不要做一般人。

Trust me. This is good advice.
相信我。這些是很好的建議。

III. 短篇作文：

Advice You Can Trust

　　Here is some advice you can trust. *First, don't abandon* your morals. Don't *abuse* your authority. Don't *ambush* people or be a backstabber. *Remember that arguing* doesn't improve a situation. If you *assault* somebody, you might wind up in jail. And do yourself a favor and don't *assume* you're always right. *Above all*, don't let anything *annoy* you. Don't *alienate* yourself from potential supporters. *Be* an above *average* person and enjoy your life.

A

你可以信任的建議

　　以下是一些你可以信任的建議。第一，不要放棄你的道德標準。不要濫用你的權力。不要暗算別人，或在背後捅人一刀。要記得，爭論無法改善情況。如果你攻擊別人，最後可能會坐牢。並且幫你自己一個忙，不要以爲自己永遠是對的。最重要的是，不要讓任何事情使你心煩。不要使自己疏遠潛在的支持者。要比一般人好，並享受你的生活。

* authority〔ɔ'θɔrətɪ〕 *n.* 權威；權力
  backstabber〔'bæk,stæbɚ〕 *n.* 在背後捅一刀的人　　***wind up*** 最後
  jail〔dʒel〕 *n.* 監獄　　potential〔pə'tɛnʃəl〕 *adj.* 潛在的；可能的

IV. 填空：

　　First of all, don't ___1___ a friend or family member who's in trouble. Don't ___2___ others or treat them poorly. Don't ___3___ people when they aren't paying attention.

　　Likewise, don't waste time ___4___ with people. Don't let yourself be ___5___ by a bully. Don't ___6___ or take anything for granted.

　　On top of that, don't have a lot of ___7___ habits. Don't ___8___ yourself from friends. And finally, don't be an ___9___ person.

　　首先，不要抛棄在困難中的朋友或家人。不要虐待別人，或對別人不好。不要在別人不注意時，暗算他們。

　　同樣地，不要浪費時間和人爭論。不要讓自己被惡霸攻擊。不要自以爲是，或把任何事都視爲理所當然。

　　此外，不要有很多令人心煩的習慣。不要使自己和朋友疏遠。最後，不要做一般人。

【解答】 1. abandon　2. abuse　3. ambush　4. arguing　5. assaulted
　　　　 6. assume　7. annoying　8. alienate　9. average
* ***pay attention*** 注意　　bully〔'bʊlɪ〕 *n.* 惡霸
  take…for granted 把…視爲理所當然

A

V. 詞彙題：

Directions: *Choose the one word that best completes the sentence.*

1. Your goals and dreams should never be _____.
   (A) absorbed　(B) accepted　(C) abandoned　(D) accorded

2. The wise man never _____ his authority.
   (A) aches　(B) abuses　(C) addicts　(D) abounds

3. Don't allow yourself to be _____ by the enemy.
   (A) advertised　(B) afforded　(C) allowed　(D) ambushed

4. The less you _____ with people, the better you'll feel.
   (A) argue　(B) amaze　(C) arouse　(D) approach

5. If you _____ someone, you might end up in jail.
   (A) ascend　(B) assess　(C) assault　(D) associate

6. It's dangerous to _____ that nothing can go wrong.
   (A) assign　(B) assume　(C) assemble　(D) assist

7. If you _____ people, they won't want to be your friend.
   (A) attach　(B) assure　(C) annoy　(D) attract

8. It's very easy to _____ people with a bad attitude.
   (A) authorize　(B) award　(C) announce　(D) alienate

9. _____ people live mediocre lives.
   (A) Average　(B) Atomic　(C) Aware　(D) Annual

【答案】1.(C)　2.(B)　3.(D)　4.(A)　5.(C)　6.(B)
　　　　7.(C)　8.(D)　9.(A)

A

VI. 同義字整理：

1. **abandon** 〔 ə'bændən 〕 *v.*
   抛棄
   - = leave 〔 liv 〕
   - = forake 〔 fə'sek 〕
   - = give up
   - = turn your back on

2. **abuse** 〔 ə'bjuz 〕 *v.* 虐待
   - = hurt 〔 hɜt 〕
   - = harm 〔 harm 〕
   - = injure 〔 'ɪndʒə 〕
   - = damage 〔 'dæmɪdʒ 〕

3. **ambush** 〔 'æmbʊʃ 〕 *v.* 埋伏；
   暗算
   - = trap 〔 træp 〕
   - = attack 〔 ə'tæk 〕
   - = surprise 〔 sə'praɪz 〕

4. **argue** 〔 'ɑrgju 〕 *v.* 爭論
   - = fight 〔 faɪt 〕
   - = dispute 〔 dɪ'spjut 〕
   - = quarrel 〔 'kwɔrəl 〕

5. **assault** 〔 ə'sɔlt 〕 *v. n.* 攻擊
   - = beat 〔 bit 〕
   - = strike 〔 straɪk 〕
   - = attack 〔 ə'tæk 〕

6. **assume** 〔 ə's(j)um 〕 *v.* 假定；
   認爲
   - = presume 〔 prɪ'zum 〕
   - = suppose 〔 sə'poz 〕
   - = believe 〔 bɪ'liv 〕
   - = think 〔 θɪŋk 〕

7. **annoy** 〔 ə'nɔɪ 〕 *v.* 使心煩
   - = disturb 〔 dɪ'stɜb 〕
   - = harass 〔 hə'ræs 〕
   - = provoke 〔 prə'vok 〕
   - = irritate 〔 'ɪrə,tet 〕
   - = anger 〔 'æŋgə 〕

8. **alienate** 〔 'eljən,et 〕 *v.* 使疏遠
   - = divide 〔 də'vaɪd 〕
   - = separate 〔 'sɛpə,ret 〕
   - = antagonize 〔 æn'tægə,naɪz 〕

9. **average** 〔 'ævərɪdʒ 〕 *adj.* 平均的；
   一般的
   - = common 〔 'kamən 〕
   - = normal 〔 'nɔrml̩ 〕
   - = regular 〔 'rɛgjələ 〕
   - = ordinary 〔 'ɔrdn̩,ɛrɪ 〕
   - = mediocre 〔 ,midɪ'okə 〕

Good Advice: What Not to Do

2. B

看英文唸出中文	一口氣說九句	看中文唸出英文
beg[2] 〔 bɛg 〕v.	字首是 be {	**Don't *beg*.** 不要乞討。	乞討
betray[6] 〔 bɪ'tre 〕v.		***Betray* others.** 不要背叛別人。	出賣
boast[4] 〔 bost 〕v.		***Boast*.** 不要自誇。	自誇
bribe[5] 〔 braɪb 〕v.		***Bribe*.** 不要賄賂。	賄賂
blame[3] 〔 blem 〕v.		***Blame* others.** 不要責備別人。	責備
break down 	字首是 br {	***Break down*.** 不要崩潰。	崩潰
brutal[4] 〔'brutḷ〕adj.		**Don't be *brutal*.** 不要殘忍。	殘忍的
burden[3] 〔'bɝdṇ〕n.	字首是 bur {	**Don't be a *burden*.** 不要成為負擔。	負擔
burn[2] 〔 bɝn 〕v.		**Don't *burn* your bridges.** 不要斷自己的後路。	燃燒

I. 背景說明：

B

    Don't beg. 可說成：***Don't beg*** for anything.（不要乞討任何東西。）***Don't beg*** for money.（不要乞討錢。）***Don't beg*** or borrow.（不要要錢或借錢。）*Betray others.* 在此共用前面的 Don't，即 Don't ***betray others***.（不要背叛別人。）Don't ***betray*** your friends.（不要背叛你的朋友。）Don't ***betray*** yourself.（不要背叛自己。）（ = *Don't harm yourself.* 不要傷害自己。）*Boast* 在此指 Don't ***boast***.（不要自誇。）Don't ***boast*** of your success.（不要吹噓自己的成功。）Don't brag or ***boast***.（不要自吹自擂。）【brag〔bræg〕*v.* 吹噓；自誇】

    Bribe. 在此指 Don't ***bribe***.（不要賄賂。）Don't try to ***bribe*** people.（不要想去賄賂別人。）Don't allow yourself to be ***bribed***.（不要容許自己被賄賂。）*Blame others.* 在此指 Don't ***blame others***.（不要責備別人。）Don't ***blame*** other people for your mistakes.（不要因為自己的錯誤而責備別人。）*Blame* yourself when you make a mistake.（當你犯了錯要歸咎自己。）blame 的意思有：「責備；指責；歸咎」。*Break down.* 在此指 Don't ***break down***.（不要崩潰。）Don't ***break down*** and cry.（不要情緒失控，開始哭。）（ = *Don't break down in tears.* ）break down 的意思有：①損壞；拋錨 ②分解 ③（關係或討論）破裂；失敗 ④崩潰；開始哭；情緒失控 ⑤拆毀 ⑥掃除（障礙）；排除（困難）。

    Don't be brutal. （ = *Don't be a brutal person.* 不要做一個殘忍的人。）Don't treat others ***brutally***.（不要粗暴地對待他人。）***Don't be a burden.*** 可說成：***Don't be a burden*** on others.

（不要成為別人的負擔。）Shoulder your own *burden*.（要承擔你自己的負擔。）【shoulder〔ˈʃoldɚ〕*v.* 承擔；負擔】*Don't burn your bridges*. 字面的意思是「不要燒了你的橋。」引申為「不要斷了自己的後路。」【*burn one's bridges* 自斷一切退路；義無反顧】例如你在公司上班，跟公司鬧翻離開，就沒辦法再回去了。最好要保持關係（Maintain relationships.），不要製造敵人（Don't make enemies.）。

> 【比較】　*Don't burn your bridges*.【正】
> 　　　　*Don't burn your bridge*.【誤】
> 　　　　說英文，差一個字母就錯，用背的語言，
> 　　　　說起來最有信心。

Ladies and gentlemen:

Don't beg.
Betray others.
Boast.

Bribe.
Blame others.
Break down.

Don't be brutal.
Don't a burden.
Don't burn your bridges.

*Follow this advice and
be a happy person.*

Ⅱ. 短篇英語演講：

B

> ***Ladies and gentlemen:*** 各位先生，各位女士：
>
> ***Don't beg*** for anything. 不要乞討任何東西。
> Don't ***betray others***. 不要背叛別人。
> Don't ***boast*** of your success. 不要吹噓自己的成功。
>
> Don't try to ***bribe*** people. 不要想去賄賂別人。
> Don't ***blame others*** for your mistakes.
> 不要因為自己的錯誤而責備別人。
> Don't ***break down*** and cry. 不要情緒失控，開始哭。
>
> ***Don't be*** a ***brutal*** person. 不要做一個殘忍的人。
> ***Don't be a burden*** on others. 不要成為別人的負擔。
> ***Don't burn your bridges***. 不要斷了自己的後路。
>
> ***Follow this advice and be a happy person***.
> 聽從這些建議，做一個快樂的人。

Ⅲ. 短篇作文：

Advice to Be Happy

If you want to be a happy person, ***don't beg*** or borrow from people. Don't ***betray*** your morals and ethics. *Also*, don't brag or ***boast*** about your achievements. *At the same time*, don't allow yourself to be ***bribed***. ***Blame*** only yourself when you make a mistake. Don't ***break down*** in tears. *Of course*, don't treat others ***brutally***. Shoulder your own ***burden***. *Finally*, don't make enemies by ***burning your bridges***, and you'll definitely be happy.

快樂的建議

　　如果你想做一個快樂的人，就不要向人要錢或借錢。不要背叛你的道德標準和倫理規範。此外，不要吹噓你的成就。同時，不要容許自己被賄賂。當你犯了錯，只能歸咎自己。不要情緒失控，開始哭。當然，不要粗暴地對待他人。要承擔你自己的負擔。最後，不要斷了自己的後路，製造敵人，那樣你一定會快樂

* morals (ˋmɔrəlz) *n. pl.* 道德觀念　　ethics (ˋεθɪks) *n. pl.* 倫理；道德規範
in tears 流著淚；哭泣著　　definitely (ˋdεfənɪtlɪ) *adv.* 一定

IV. 填空：

　　For starters, don't ___1___ anybody for anything. Don't ___2___ your friends or confidants. Don't brag or ___3___ of your success.

　　Additionally, don't try to ___4___ people with money or special favors. Don't ___5___ other people for your mistakes. Don't ___6___ and cry.

　　Most of all, don't be a ___7___ and violent person. Don't be a ___8___ on others. Treat people fairly, don't ___9___ your bridges, and you'll be a happy person.

　　首先，不要向任何人乞討任何東西。不要背叛你的朋友或知已。不要吹噓自己的成功。

　　此外，不要想用錢或特別的禮物來賄賂別人。不要因為自己的錯誤而責備別人。不要情緒失控，開始哭。

　　最重要的是，不要做一個殘忍又粗暴的人。不要成為別人的負擔。要公平地對待別人，不要斷了自己的後路，那樣你就會是一個快樂的人。

【解答】 1. beg　2. betray　3. boast　4. bribe　5. blame
　　　　6. break down　7. brutal　8. burden　9. burn
　　*　**for starters** 首先　　confidant (ˏkɑnfəˋdænt) *n.* 知己
　　　favor (ˋfevɚ) *n.* 恩惠；禮物
　　　violent (ˋvaɪələnt) *adj.* 暴力的；粗暴的

V. 詞彙題：

Directions: *Choose the one word that best completes the sentence.*

B

1. The worst thing you can do is _____ someone to help you out.
   (A) bake (B) bang (C) beg (D) bear

2. Don't be seen as having _____ your friends.
   (A) behaved (B) betrayed (C) belonged (D) barked

3. People who _____ and brag are fools.
   (A) bind (B) beckon (C) blink (D) boast

4. He _____ them to vote for him.
   (A) bribed (B) bleached (C) blended (D) boiled

5. _____ others for one's mistake is the sign of a coward.
   (A) Boarding (B) Boosting (C) Breathing (D) Blaming

6. Many people _____ due to the pressures of life.
   (A) break out (B) break down (C) break in
   (D) break even

7. A _____ man is feared but not respected.
   (A) brisk (B) broad (C) brutal (D) blunt

8. Everybody has a _____ to carry and you're no exception.
   (A) burden (B) behalf (C) bazaar (D) bowel

9. If you _____ your bridges, you can't ever go back.
   (A) breed (B) burn (C) bully (D) bury

【答案】 1.（C） 2.（B） 3.（D） 4.（A） 5.（D） 6.（B）
　　　　 7.（C） 8.（A） 9.（B）

B

VI. 同義字整理：

1. **beg** 〔 bɛg 〕 *v.* 乞討；乞求
   - = request 〔 rɪ'kwɛst 〕
   - = implore 〔 ɪm'plor 〕
   - = plead with

2. **betray** 〔 bɪ'tre 〕 *v.* 出賣
   - = be disloyal to
   - = be unfaithful to
   - = give away
   - = stab in the back

3. **boast** 〔 bost 〕 *v.* 自誇
   - = brag 〔 bræg 〕
   - = bluster 〔 'blʌstɚ 〕
   - = talk big

4. **bribe** 〔 braɪb 〕 *v.* 賄賂
   - = buy off
   - = pay off
   - = reward 〔 rɪ'wɔrd 〕

5. **blame** 〔 blem 〕 *v.* 責備
   - = condemn 〔 kən'dɛm 〕
   - = accuse 〔 ə'kjuz 〕
   - = charge 〔 tʃɑrdʒ 〕
   - = hold responsible

6. **break down** 崩潰
   - = collapse 〔 kə'læps 〕
   - = destroy 〔 dɪ'strɔɪ 〕
   - = give way
   - = become distressed or upset

7. **brutal** 〔 'brutḷ 〕 *adj.* 殘忍的
   - = cruel 〔 'kruəl 〕
   - = savage 〔 'sævɪdʒ 〕
   - = vicious 〔 'vɪʃəs 〕

   - = harsh 〔 hɑrʃ 〕
   - = ruthless 〔 'ruθlɪs 〕

8. **burden** 〔 'bɝdṇ 〕 *n.* 負擔
   - = weight 〔 wet 〕
   - = stress 〔 strɛs 〕
   - = strain 〔 stren 〕

   - = trouble 〔 'trʌbḷ 〕
   - = responsibility 〔 rɪ,spɑnsə'bɪlətɪ 〕

9. **Don't burn your bridges.**
   不要斷了自己的後路。
   - = Always leave a way out.
   - = Leave a situation in good standing.
   - = Keep your options open.

Good Advice: What Not to Do

3. C (1)

看英文唸出中文	一口氣說九句	看中文唸出英文
conflict[2]	字首是 con { Don't start *conflict*.	衝突
〔ˈkɑnflɪkt 〕 *n.*	不要先引起衝突。	
conceal[5]	*Conceal*.	隱瞞
〔 kənˈsil 〕 *v.*	不要隱瞞。	
condemn[5]	*Condemn*.	譴責
〔 kənˈdɛm 〕 *v.*	不要罵人。	

cry[1]	由短到長 { *Cry*.	哭
〔 kraɪ 〕 *v.*	不要哭。	
curse[4]	*Curse*.	詛咒
〔 kɝs 〕 *v. n.*	不要罵髒話。	
criticize[4]	*Criticize*.	批評
〔ˈkrɪtəˌsaɪz 〕 *v.*	不要批評。	

cheat[2]	字首是 Compl { *Cheat*.	欺騙
〔 tʃit 〕 *v.*	不要欺騙。	
complain[2]	*Complain*.	抱怨
〔 kəmˈplen 〕 *v.*	不要抱怨。	
complicate[4]	*Complicate* things.	使複雜
〔ˈkɑmpləˌket 〕 *v.*	不要把事情複雜化。	

I. 背景説明：

Don't start conflict. 可説成：
Don't initiate *conflict*.（不要先引
起衝突。）Don't cause *conflict*.
（不要引起衝突。）*Conceal*. 在此
指 Don't *conceal*.（不要隱瞞。）
Don't *conceal* the truth.（不要隱
瞞眞相。）Don't *conceal* your
motives.（不要隱瞞你的動機。）

Condemn. 在此指 Don't *condemn*.（不要罵人。）Don't
condemn others.（不要譴責他人。）Don't be quick to
condemn people.（不要立刻罵人。）別人犯了錯誤，不要
立刻罵，等一段時間較好。

Cry. 在此指 Don't *cry*.（不要哭。）Don't *cry* over
spilt milk.（【諺】木已成舟；已成定局。）Don't let
anybody make you *cry*.（不要讓任何人讓你哭。）

Curse. 在此指 Don't *curse*.（不要咒罵。）也就是「不要
罵髒話。」(= *Don't use offensive or impolite language*.)
Don't *curse* or swear.（不要罵髒話。）【swear〔swer〕*v*. 發
誓；咒罵】Don't *curse* people in public.（不要當衆用髒話
罵人。）curse 的主要意思是「詛咒」，在此指「咒罵；罵
髒話」。*Criticize*. 在此指 Don't *criticize*.（不要批評。）
Don't *criticize* others.（不要批評別人。）Try helping
instead of *criticizing*.（要努力幫助而不是批評。）

Cheat. 在此指 Don't *cheat*.（不要欺騙。）Don't *cheat* people.（不要騙人。）*Cheating* is bad.（騙人不好。）*Complain*. 在此指 Don't *complain*.（不要抱怨。）Don't *complain* about your problems.（不要抱怨你的問題。）Don't be a person who *complains* all the time.（不要做一個老是抱怨的人。）*Complicate things*. 在此指 Don't *complicate things*.（不要把事情複雜化。）(= *Don't complicate matters*.) Lying only *complicates* your life.（說謊只會使你的生活變得複雜。）

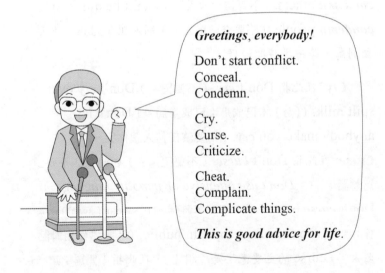

Greetings, *everybody!*

Don't start conflict.
Conceal.
Condemn.

Cry.
Curse.
Criticize.

Cheat.
Complain.
Complicate things.

This is good advice for life.

C

II. 短篇英語演講：

Greetings, everybody! 大家好！

Don't start conflict. 不要先引起衝突。
Don't *conceal* the truth. 不要隱瞞眞相。
Don't be quick to *condemn* people. 不要立刻罵人。

Don't let anybody make you *cry*. 不要讓任何人讓你哭。
Don't *curse* people in public. 不要當衆用髒話罵人。
Don't *criticize* others. 不要批評別人。

Don't *cheat* people. 不要騙人。
Don't *complain* about your problems.
不要抱怨你的問題。
Don't *complicate things*. 不要把事情複雜化。

This is good advice for life. 這是對人生很好的建議。

III. 短篇作文：

Good Advice for Life

Do you want some good advice for life? Number one:
Don't start conflict. Don't *conceal* your motives. Don't
condemn others. *Moreover*, don't *cry* over spilt milk.
Don't *curse* people with offensive or impolite language.
Try helping instead of *criticizing*. *Obviously*, *cheating* is
bad. *Likewise*, don't be a person who *complains* all the
time. *And* remember, lying only *complicates* your life.

對人生很好的建議

你想要一些對人生很好的建議嗎？第一：不要先引起衝突。不要隱瞞你的動機。不要譴責他人。此外，覆水難收。不要用令人不愉快或無禮的語言罵人。要努力幫助而不是批評。顯然，騙人是不好的。同樣地，不要做一個老是抱怨的人。而且要記得，說謊只會使你的生活變得複雜。

* motive〔ˈmotɪv〕*n.* 動機　　spill〔spɪl〕*v.* 灑出
offensive〔əˈfɛnsɪv〕*adj.* 令人不愉快的　　***instead of*** 而不是

IV. 填空：

First, don't be a person who initiates ___1___. Don't ___2___ the truth or distort the facts. Don't be quick to ___3___ people.

Besides, don't let anybody make you ___4___. Don't ___5___ or swear at people in public. Don't ___6___ others for making a mistake.

Of course, don't ___7___ people out of their money. Don't ___8___ about your problems. Most importantly, don't ___9___ matters by being a difficult person.

　　首先，不要做一個會先引起衝突的人。不要隱瞞真相或扭曲事實。不要立刻罵人。

　　此外，不要讓任何人讓你哭。不要當眾用髒話罵人。不要因為犯錯而批評別人。

　　當然，不要騙別人的錢。不要抱怨你的問題。最重要的是，不要做一個難相處的人，把事情複雜化。

【解答】 1. conflict　2. conceal　3. condemn　4. cry　5. curse
　　　　 6. criticize　7. cheat　8. complain　9. complicate

* initiate〔ɪˈnɪʃɪˌet〕*v.* 開始；創始
distort〔dɪsˈtɔrt〕*v.* 扭曲　　***in public*** 公開地
difficult〔ˈdɪfəˌkʌlt〕*adj.* 難相處的

V. 詞彙題：

Directions: *Choose the one word that best completes the sentence.*

1. Starting _____ is a sure way to make enemies.
   (A) concern   (B) conflict   (C) concept   (D) contact

2. You can _____ the facts, but the truth will always come out.
   (A) consult   (B) consume   (C) conceal   (D) console

3. It's better to pity than _____ your enemies.
   (A) continue   (B) condemn   (C) consist   (D) confess

4. It's OK to _____ sometimes, but you really should learn to control your emotions.
   (A) camp   (B) chew   (C) cast   (D) cry

5. In some countries, it's against the law to _____ in public.
   (A) curse   (B) cancel   (C) carve   (D) cease

6. Think about how you would feel if you were the one being _____.
   (A) commuted   (B) criticized   (C) coincided   (D) circulated

7. If you have to _____, you will never truly win the game.
   (A) cheat   (B) cherish   (C) chant   (D) charge

8. Be grateful for what you have and stop _____.
   (A) comprising   (B) completing   (C) complaining
   (D) combining

9. Don't _____ your life by getting involved with bad people.
   (A) compute   (B) compose   (C) compete   (D) complicate

【答案】 1.（B） 2.（C） 3.（B） 4.（D） 5.（A） 6.（B）
        7.（A） 8.（C） 9.（D）

VI. 同義字整理：

1. conflict ('kɑnflɪkt) n. 衝突

= fight (faɪt)
= dispute (dɪ'spjut)
= clash (klæʃ)

= difference ('dɪfrəns)
= disagreement (,dɪsə'grimənt)

2. conceal (kən'sil) v. 隱藏

= hide (haɪd)
= cover ('kʌvɚ)
= keep secret

= disguise (dɪs'gaɪz)
= suppress (sə'prɛs)

3. condemn (kən'dɛm) v. 譴責

= denounce (dɪ'naʊns)
= criticize ('krɪtə,saɪz)
= blame (blem)

4. cry (kraɪ) v. 哭

= weep (wip)
= sob (sɑb)
= whine (hwaɪn)
= shed tears

5. curse (kɝs) v. n. 詛咒；咒罵

= swear (swɛr)
= use bad language
= be foul-mouthed

6. criticize ('krɪtə,saɪz) v. 批評

= condemn (kən'dɛm)
= put down
= find fault with
= disapprove of

7. cheat (tʃit) v. 欺騙；作弊

= fool (ful)
= trick (trɪk)
= deceive (dɪ'siv)
= mislead (mɪs'lid)

8. complain (kəm'plen) v. 抱怨

= grumble ('grʌmbl̩)
= groan (gron)
= whine (hwaɪn)
= find fault

9. complicate ('kɑmplə,ket) v. 使複雜

= confuse (kən'fjuz)
= make difficult
= make intricate

Good Advice: What Not to Do

4. C (2)

看英文唸出中文	一口氣說九句	看中文唸出英文
choke³ 〔 tʃok 〕*v.*	Don't *choke*. 不要驚慌出錯。	噎住
confuse³ 〔 kənˈfjuz 〕*v.*	字首是 con { Don't get *confused*. 不要糊里糊塗。	使困惑
contradictory⁶ 〔͵kɑntrəˈdɪktərɪ 〕*adj.*	Don't be *contradictory*. 不要唱反調。	相互矛盾的
cheap² 〔 tʃip 〕*adj.*	字首是 Ch { *Cheap*. 不要小氣。	便宜的；小氣的
childish² 〔ˈtʃaɪldɪʃ 〕*adj.*	*Childish*. 不要幼稚。	幼稚的
conceited⁶ 〔 kənˈsitɪd 〕*adj.*	字首是 Co { *Conceited*. 不要自大。	自負的
corrupt⁵ 〔 kəˈrʌpt 〕*adj.*	*Corrupt*. 不要貪污。	貪污的
critical⁴ 〔ˈkrɪtɪkl̟ 〕*adj.*	*Critical*. 不要愛批評。	批評的
contrary⁴ 〔ˈkɑntrɛrɪ 〕*adj.*	*Contrary*. 不要為反對而反對。 (= *Contradictory*.)	相反的

I. 背景説明：

Don't choke. 主要的意思是「不要噎到。」(= *Don't fail to breathe, swallow or talk.*) 當某人吃太快，你就可以跟他説：You're going to *choke.*（你會噎到。）*Don't choke.* 在這裡的意思是「不要驚慌出錯。」(= *Don't fail to perform due to anxiety.*) choke 的意思有：「噎住；使窒息；出錯」。Don't *choke* at the big moment.（在重要的時刻不要驚慌出錯。）Don't *choke* when it's your turn to shine.（當輪到你要發光、發亮的時候，不要驚慌出錯。）*Don't get confused.*（頭腦要清楚。）(= *Keep your mind clear.*) 可説成：Don't be a *confused* person.（不要頭腦搞不清楚。）Don't be *confused* by new information.（不要被新的資訊搞糊塗。）(= *Don't let new information confuse you.*)【在此不可説 the information】confused 在此可當純粹形容詞，作「困惑的；混淆的」解。confuse 這個字是動詞，作「使困惑；使混淆」解。如：Don't *confuse* this with that.（這個和那個不要搞不清楚。）*Don't be contradictory.* (= *Don't be a contradictory person.*) contradictory 的意思有「好反駁的；愛爭辯的；互相矛盾的」。Avoid making *contradictory* statements.（要避免有相互矛盾的説法。）有一種人什麼都反對，就是 a contradictory person (= *a person who never agrees*)，這種人，人人討厭，千萬做不得。Regardless of right or wrong, they will *contradict* you.（不管對或錯，他們總是會反駁你。）

Cheap. 在此指 Don't be *cheap*.（不要小氣。）（= *Don't be a cheap person.*）cheap 的主要意思是「便宜的」，在此作「小氣的；吝嗇的」解。Don't be *cheap* or stingy.（不要小氣。）（= *Don't be tight with your money.*）*Childish.* 在此指 Don't be *childish*.（不要幼稚。）Don't act *childish*.（行為舉止不要幼稚。）（= *Don't behave childishly.*）*Conceited.* 在此指 Don't be *conceited*.（= *Don't act conceited.*）（不要自大。）conceited 的意思有：「自負的；自大的；驕傲自滿的」。這個字很特殊，是由名詞 conceit 轉變而來的形容詞，其他還有 good-hearted（好心的）、absent-minded（心不在焉的）等。

　　Corrupt. 在此指 Don't be *corrupt*.（不要貪污。）Don't allow yourself to be *corrupt*.（不要讓自己貪污。）可加強語氣說成：Don't ever be *corrupt*.（永遠不要貪污。）*Corrupt* people never win.（貪污的人永遠不會是贏家。）corrupt 可作「貪污的」、「腐敗的」解。*Critical.* 在此指 Don't be *critical*.（不要批評。）（= *Don't be a critical person.*）critical 的意思有：「批評的；挑剔的；關鍵的；危急的」。Don't be overly *critical* of people.（不要對人太過挑剔。）*Contrary.* 在此指 Don't be *contrary*.（不要為反對而反對。）（= *Don't be a contrary person. = Don't be contradictory.*）Don't say things just to be *contrary*.（不要為了反對而反對。）

II. 英語演講：

【一字英語演講】

【短篇英語演講】

My dearest friends:

My dearest friends: 我最親愛的朋友們：

Don't choke.
Don't get confused.
Don't be
  contradictory.

Don't choke at the big moment.
在重要的時刻不要驚慌出錯。
Don't get confused by new information.
不要被新的資訊搞糊塗。
Don't be a *contradictory* person.
不要做一個什麼都反對的人。

Cheap.
Childish.
Conceited.

Don't be *cheap* or stingy.　不要小氣。
Don't behave *childishly.*　行為舉止不要幼稚。
Don't act *conceited.*　不要表現得很自大。

Corrupt.
Critical.
Contrary.

Don't allow yourself to be *corrupt.*
不要讓自己貪污。
Don't be a *critical* person.　不要做一個愛批評的人。
Don't be *contrary.*　不要為反對而反對。

Follow this advice
  to happiness and
  success.

Follow this advice to happiness and success.
要聽從這些會讓你快樂又成功的建議。

III. 短篇作文：

Advice for Happiness and Success

　　Happiness and success can be yours if you *don't choke* when
it's your turn to shine.　Keep a clear mind so you *don't get*
confused.　Avoid making *contradictory* statements.　*Meanwhile*,
don't be *cheap* or stingy.　Try not to act *childishly.*　*Additionally*,
don't be an arrogant or *conceited* person.　Don't be *corrupt.*　Don't
be overly *critical* of people.　*Finally*, don't say things just to be
contrary, and happiness and success will be yours.

讓你快樂又成功的建議

當輪到你要發光、發亮的時候，如果你能不驚慌出錯，那快樂和成功就會是你的。頭腦要清楚，這樣你就不會混淆。要避免有相互矛盾的說法。同時，不要小氣。行為舉止儘量不要幼稚。此外，不要做一個傲慢或自大的人。不要貪污。不要對人太過挑剔。最後，不要為了反對而反對，那樣你就會快樂又成功。

> * *it's your turn* 輪到你了   act〔ækt〕*v.* 舉止；表現得
> arrogant〔'ærəgənt〕*adj.* 傲慢的

IV. 填空：

To begin with, don't ___1___ at the big moment. Don't be ___2___ by new information. Don't be a ___3___ person who likes to argue.

Additionally, don't be a ___4___ or stingy person. Don't behave in a ___5___ manner. Don't act ___6___, like you're better than everyone else.

To sum up, don't allow yourself to be ___7___. Don't be a ___8___ person. Don't be a ___9___ character, and you'll be happy and successful.

首先，在重要的時刻不要驚慌出錯。不要被新的資訊搞糊塗。不要做一個什麼都反對，喜歡爭論的人。

此外，不要做一個小氣的人。行為舉止不要幼稚。不要表現得很自大，像是你比任何人都好。

總之，不要讓自己貪污。不要做一個挑剔的人。不要做一個為反對而反對的人，那樣你就會快樂又成功。

【解答】1. choke   2. confused   3. contradictory   4. cheap
　　　　5. childish   6. conceited   7. corrupt   8. critical
　　　　9. contrary

* stingy〔'stɪndʒɪ〕*adj.* 小氣的   manner〔'mænɚ〕*n.* 樣子

V. 詞彙題：

Directions: *Choose the one word that best completes the sentence.*

1. Fear of making a mistake is what causes people to _____.
   (A) choke   (B) conduct   (C) confirm   (D) compare

2. Your mind may be _____, but your emotions will never lie to you.
   (A) coincided   (B) confused   (C) collected   (D) combated

3. There's no point in talking to a _____ person.
   (A) colloquial   (B) consistent   (C) consequent
   (D) contradictory

4. Don't waste money, but don't be _____, either.
   (A) concise   (B) contagious   (C) cheap   (D) costly

5. Crying for things you can't have is _____.
   (A) credible   (B) cultural   (C) current   (D) childish

6. Before you get _____, remember that there's always somebody better than you.
   (A) curious   (B) conceited   (C) concrete   (D) constant

7. The whole system is inefficient and _____.
   (A) corrupt   (B) clinical   (C) collective   (D) circular

8. Be as _____ of yourself as you are of other people.
   (A) classical   (B) chemical   (C) critical   (D) commercial

9. You won't make many friends by being a _____ person.
   (A) conscious   (B) considerable   (C) contrary   (D) content

【答案】 1.(A)   2.(B)   3.(D)   4.(C)   5.(D)   6.(B)
　　　　 7.(A)   8.(C)   9.(C)

VI. 同義字整理：

1. **choke** 〔 tʃok 〕 *v.* 使窒息；噎住；
出錯

> = fail 〔 fel 〕
> = fall short
> = fall through

2. **confuse** 〔 kən'fjuz 〕 *v.* 使困惑

> = bewilder 〔 bɪ'wɪldə 〕
> = puzzle 〔 'pʌzl̩ 〕
> = baffle 〔 'bæfl̩ 〕

3. **contradictory** 〔 ͵kɑntrə'dɪktərɪ 〕
adj. 相互矛盾的

> = contrary 〔 'kɑntrɛrɪ 〕
> = opposite 〔 'ɑpəzɪt 〕
> = conflicting 〔 kən'flɪktɪŋ 〕
> = inconsistent 〔 ͵ɪnkən'sɪstənt 〕

4. **cheap** 〔 tʃip 〕 *adj.* 便宜的；小氣的

> = stingy 〔 'stɪndʒɪ 〕
> = miserly 〔 'maɪzəlɪ 〕
> = ungenerous 〔 ʌn'dʒɛnərəs 〕

5. **childish** 〔 'tʃaɪldɪʃ 〕 *adj.* 幼稚的

> = immature 〔 ͵ɪmə'tʃʊr 〕
> = foolish 〔 'fulɪʃ 〕
> = silly 〔 'sɪlɪ 〕

6. **conceited** 〔 kən'sitɪd 〕 *adj.*
自負的

> = vain 〔 ven 〕
> = arrogant 〔 'ærəgənt 〕
> = immodest 〔 ɪ'mɑdɪst 〕
> = self-important
>   〔 ͵sɛlfɪm'pɔrtn̩t 〕

7. **corrupt** 〔 kə'rʌpt 〕 *adj.* 貪污的

> = rotten 〔 'rɑtn̩ 〕
> = dishonest 〔 dɪs'ɑnɪst 〕
> = fraudulent 〔 'frɔdʒələnt 〕
> = unethical 〔 ʌn'ɛθɪkl̩ 〕

8. **critical** 〔 'krɪtɪkl̩ 〕 *adj.* 批評的

> = derogatory 〔 dɪ'rɑgə͵torɪ 〕
> = faultfinding 〔 'fɔlt͵faɪndɪŋ 〕
> = disapproving
>   〔 ͵dɪsə'pruvɪŋ 〕

9. **contrary** 〔 'kɑntrɛrɪ 〕 *adj.*
相反的

> = opposite 〔 'ɑpəzɪt 〕
> = opposed 〔 ə'pozd 〕
> = contradictory
>   〔 ͵kɑntrə'dɪktərɪ 〕
> = inconsistent
>   〔 ͵ɪnkən'sɪstənt 〕

C

Good Advice: What Not to Do

5. D (1)

看英文唸出中文	一口氣說九句	看中文唸出英文
delay[2] 〔 dɪ'le 〕*v.*	字首是 de {	Don't *delay*. 不要拖延。	延遲
despair[5] 〔 dɪ'spɛr 〕*n. v.*		*Despair*. 不要絕望。	絕望
degrade[6] 〔 dɪ'gred 〕*v.*		*Degrade* others. 不要貶低別人。	降低

disturb[4] 〔 dɪ'stɝb 〕*v.*	字首是 Dis {	*Disturb* others. 不要打擾別人。	打擾
distort[6] 〔 dɪs'tɔrt 〕*v.*		*Distort* things. 不要曲解事情。	使扭曲
disregard[6] 〔 ˏdɪsrɪ'gɑrd 〕*v.*		*Disregard* others. 不要忽視別人。	忽視

discourage[4] 〔 dɪs'kɝɪdʒ 〕*v.*	都有 Don't {	*Discourage* others. 不要使人氣餒。	使氣餒
doubt[2] 〔 daut 〕*v. n.*		Don't *doubt*. 不要懷疑別人。	懷疑
defeat[4] 〔 dɪ'fit 〕*v.*		Don't be *defeated*. 不要被打敗。	打敗

I. 背景說明：

Don't delay. 可說成：*Don't delay* your work. （不要拖延你的工作。）*Don't delay* others. （不要耽擱別人；不要讓人等。）（ = *Don't cause people to wait*. ）delay 可作「延遲」、「耽擱」解。*Despair*. 在此指 Don't *despair*. （不要絕望。）Don't *despair* over a loss. （不要為了損失而絕望。）（ = *Don't despair because of a loss*. ）Don't *despair* when you're in trouble. （遇到困難時，不要絕望。）*Degrade others*. 在此指 Don't *degrade others*. （不要貶低別人。）Don't *degrade* yourself. （不要貶低自己；不要使自己丟臉。）（ = *Don't do anything shameful*. ）degrade 的主要意思是「降低」，引申為「使降級；貶低；使丟臉」。

Disturb others. 在此指 Don't *disturb others*. （不要打擾別人。）Don't *disturb* the peace. （不要擾亂安寧。）distort 的主要意思是「使扭曲」，如 A frown *distorted* her face. （皺眉頭使她的臉部扭曲。）在此作「曲解」解。*Distort things*. 是指 Don't *distort things*. （不要曲解事情。）可說成：Don't *distort* what other people say. （不要曲解別人說的話。）不可說成：*Don't distort others*.（誤）因為人無法曲解。在中文裡，不要曲解某人，意思是不要曲解某人的話。Don't *distort* the truth. （不要曲解真相。）Don't *distort* the facts. （不要扭曲事實。）*Disregard others*. 在此指 Don't *disregard others*. （不要忽視別人。）Don't *disregard* the rules. （不要忽視規定。）Don't *disregard* the safety of others. （不要忽視別人的安全。）

Discourage others. 在此指 Don't *discourage others.*（不要使人氣餒。）discourage 的主要意思是「使氣餒」，也可作「使打消念頭；阻止」解。Don't *discourage* people from trying something new.（不要阻止別人嘗試新事物。）*Don't doubt.*（不要懷疑別人。）(= *Don't doubt others.*) **Don't doubt** others' good intentions.（不要懷疑別人的好意。）*Don't doubt* yourself.（不要懷疑自己。）(= *Believe in yourself.* 要相信自己的能力。）Don't let *doubt* keep you from trying.（不要讓懷疑阻止你去嘗試。）【*keep sb. from V-ing* 阻止某人做某事】*Don't be defeated.*（不要被打敗。）*Don't be defeated* by life.（不要被生活打敗。）*Don't* allow yourself to *be defeated.*（不要讓自己被打敗。）

D

Welcome, all:

Don't delay.
Despair.
Degrade others.

Disturb others.
Distort things.
Disregard others.

Discourage others.
Don't doubt.
Don't be defeated.

Follow my suggestions to be successful.

II. 短篇英語演講：

Welcome, *all:* 歡迎大家：

Don't delay your work.　不要拖延你的工作。
Don't *despair* over a loss.　不要爲了損失而絕望。
Don't *degrade others*.　不要貶低別人。

Don't *disturb others*.　不要打擾別人。
Don't *distort things*.　不要曲解事情。
Don't *disregard others*.　不要忽視別人。

Don't *discourage others*.　不要使人氣餒。
Don't doubt others' good intentions.　不要懷疑別人的好意。
Don't allow yourself to *be defeated*.　不要讓自己被打敗。

Follow my suggestions to be successful.
聽從我的建議就會成功。

III. 短篇作文：

Suggestions for Success

You want to be successful but you need some suggestions.
First, *don't delay* others who have somewhere to be. Don't
despair when you're in trouble. Don't do anything shameful
to *degrade* yourself. *Next*, don't *disturb others*. Don't *distort*
what other people say. Don't *disregard* the safety of *others*.
Of course, don't *discourage* or *doubt* yourself. *Above all*,
don't allow yourself to *be defeated* by life, and you will find
success.

成功的建議

你想要成功，但需要一些建議。首先，不要耽擱要去某個地方的人。遇到困難時，不要絕望。不要做任何丟臉的事，貶低自己。其次，不要打擾別人。不要曲解別人說的話。不要忽視別人的安全。當然，不要使自己氣餒或懷疑自己。最重要的是，不要讓自己被生活打敗，那樣你就會成功。

* shameful〔'ʃemfəl〕*adj.* 可恥的；丟臉的

IV. 填空：

First of all, don't ___1___ or put off your work for another time. Don't ___2___ over a loss. Don't ___3___ others with foul criticism.

Moreover, don't do anything to ___4___ the peace. Don't ___5___ the truth. Don't ___6___ the rules and cause trouble for yourself.

On top of that, don't ___7___ people from pursuing their dreams. Don't ___8___ others' good intentions. Don't allow yourself to be ___9___ and you'll find success.

首先，不要把你的工作拖延到另一個時間。不要為了損失而絕望。不要用惡意的批評貶低別人。

還有，不要做任何會擾亂安寧的事。不要扭曲事實。不要忽視規定，為自己製造麻煩。

此外，不要阻止別人追求夢想。不要懷疑別人的好意。不要讓自己被打敗，這樣你就會成功。

【解答】 1. delay　2. despair　3. degrade　4. disturb　5. distort
　　　　 6. disregard　7. discourage　8. doubt　9. defeated

* ***put off*** 拖延　　foul〔faul〕*adj.* 邪惡的；下流的
　　criticism〔'krɪtə,sɪzəm〕*n.* 批評
　　intention〔ɪn'tɛnʃən〕*n.* 意圖

V. 詞彙題：

Directions: Choose the one word that best completes the sentence.

1. The longer you _____ a project, the harder it is to finish.
   (A) depend   (B) deny   (C) derive   (D) delay

2. Never _____ of the future while you still have hope.
   (A) despair   (B) depict   (C) deliver   (D) deserve

3. _____ others says more about you than the people you're insulting.
   (A) Detecting   (B) Degrading   (C) Devising   (D) Departing

4. No good ever came from _____ a sleeping dog.
   (A) distrusting   (B) discovering   (C) dismissing
   (D) disturbing

5. Words and ideas are easily_____, but facts cannot be changed.
   (A) dodged   (B) dissolved   (C) distorted   (D) distracted

6. By _____ the rules, you put yourself in harm's way.
   (A) disposing   (B) disregarding   (C) dissuading
   (D) dispatching

7. Why _____ others from pursuing their dreams?
   (A) discourage   (B) displace   (C) disgust   (D) displease

8. No one _____ the need for improvement.
   (A) dozes   (B) dooms   (C) donates   (D) doubts

9. No person can be _____ if his spirit is still willing to fight.
   (A) dreaded   (B) defeated   (C) decorated   (D) debated

【答案】1.(D)　2.(A)　3.(B)　4.(D)　5.(C)　6.(B)
　　　　7.(A)　8.(D)　9.(B)

VI. 同義字整理：

1. **delay** 〔 dɪ'le 〕 v. 延遲
   - = postpone 〔 post'pon 〕
   - = suspend 〔 sə'spɛnd 〕
   - = put off
   - = hold back

2. **despair** 〔 dɪ'spɛr 〕 n. v. 絕望
   - = lose hope
   - = lose heart
   - = be dejected
   - = be discouraged

3. **degrade** 〔 dɪ'gred 〕 v. 降低；貶低
   - = demean 〔 dɪ'min 〕
   - = disgrace 〔 dɪs'gres 〕
   - = humiliate 〔 hju'mɪlɪ,et 〕

4. **disturb** 〔 dɪ'stɝb 〕 v. 打擾
   - = bother 〔 'baðə 〕
   - = hassle 〔 'hæsḷ 〕
   - = interrupt 〔 ,ɪntə'rʌpt 〕
   - = intrude on

5. **distort** 〔 dɪs'tɔrt 〕 v. 使扭曲
   - = twist 〔 twɪst 〕
   - = bend 〔 bɛnd 〕
   - = misinterpret 〔 ,mɪsɪn'tɝprɪt 〕

6. **disregard** 〔 ,dɪsrɪ'gard 〕 v. 忽視
   - = ignore 〔 ɪg'nor 〕
   - = neglect 〔 nɪ'glɛkt 〕
   - = overlook 〔 ,ovə'lʊk 〕
   - = take no notice of
   - = pay no attention to

7. **discourage** 〔 dɪs'kɝɪdʒ 〕 v. 使氣餒
   - = dishearten 〔 dɪs'hartṇ 〕
   - = deter 〔 dɪ'tɝ 〕
   - = prevent 〔 prɪ'vɛnt 〕
   - = dissuade 〔 dɪ'swed 〕
   - = talk out of

8. **doubt** 〔 daʊt 〕 v. n. 懷疑
   - = suspect 〔 sə'spɛkt 〕
   - = disbelieve 〔 ,dɪsbɪ'liv 〕
   - = question 〔 'kwɛstʃən 〕
   - = be skeptical
   - = be uncertain

9. **defeat** 〔 dɪ'fit 〕 v. 打敗
   - = beat 〔 bit 〕
   - = conquer 〔 'kaŋkə 〕
   - = overcome 〔 ,ovə'kʌm 〕
   - = overpower 〔 ,ovə'paʊə 〕

Good Advice: What Not to Do

6. D (2)

看英文唸出中文	一口氣說九句	看中文唸出英文
defensive[4] 〔 dɪ'fɛnsɪv 〕*adj.*	Don't be *defensive*. 不要被激怒。	防禦的；惱怒的
desperate[4] 〔'dɛspərɪt 〕*adj.*	*Desperate*. 不要絕望。	絕望的
destructive[5] 〔 dɪ'strʌktɪv 〕*adj.*	*Destructive*. 不要成 事不足，敗事有餘。	破壞性的

字首是 de

difficult[1] 〔'dɪfəˌkʌlt 〕*adj.*	*Difficult*. 不要難相處。	困難的；難相處的
dishonest[2] 〔 dɪs'ɑnɪst 〕*adj.*	*Dishonest*. 不要不誠實。	不誠實的
disgraceful[6] 〔 dɪs'gresfəl 〕*adj.*	*Disgraceful*. 不要丟臉。	可恥的

字首是 Di

dramatic[3] 〔 drə'mætɪk 〕*adj.*	*Dramatic*. 不要太激動。	戲劇性的
dreadful[5] 〔'drɛdfəl 〕*adj.*	*Dreadful*. 不要讓人害怕。	可怕的
dreary[6] 〔'drɪrɪ 〕*adj.*	*Dreary*. 不要讓人討厭。	討人厭的

字首是 Dr

D

I. 背景説明：

Don't be defensive. (= *Don't get defensive.*) 可説成：***Don't be* a *defensive* person.** (不要被激怒。) (= *Don't be irritated.*) Don't get *defensive* when someone points out your mistake. (當某人指出你的錯誤時，不要被激怒。) defensive 的

Don't be defensive.

意思有：①防禦的 (= *protective*) ②惱怒的 (= *irritated*)。 *Desperate.* 在此指 Don't be *desperate.* (不要絕望。) (= *Don't be hopeless.*) People can tell if you are *desperate.* (大家都可以看得出來你很絕望。) desperate 的意思有：①絕望的②拼命的③很想要的，要看前後句意來判斷。*Destructive.* 在此指 Don't be *destructive.* (= *Don't be a destructive person.*)「不要搞破壞。」就像中文常説的「不要成事不足，敗事有餘。」也就是 Be helpful. (要有幫助。) Don't break stuff. (不要把東西弄壞。) Don't make things worse. (不要讓事情變糟。) Get rid of *destructive* habits. (要戒除破壞性的習慣。)

Difficult. 在此指 Don't be *difficult.* (不要難相處。) (= *Don't be a difficult person.*) difficult 的主要意思是「困難的」，在此作「難相處的」解。Don't be *difficult* to deal with. (不要難相處。) *Dishonest.* 在此指 Don't be *dishonest.* (不要不誠實。) (= *Don't be a dishonest person.*)

Don't be *dishonest* with others. (不要對別人不誠實。)
Disgraceful. 在此指 Don't be *disgraceful*. (不要丟臉。)
(= *Don't be a disgraceful person*.) Avoid anything
disgraceful. (不要做任何丟臉的事。)(= *Avoid anything
shameful*.) Avoid *disgraceful* habits. (不要有丟人的習
性。) disgraceful 可作「可恥的」、「讓人丟臉的」解。

Dramatic. 在此指 Don't be *dramatic*. (不要太激動。)
(= *Don't be a dramatic person*.) Don't be very emotional.
(不要太情緒化。) dramatic 的主要意思是「戲劇性的」,
在此作「激動的」解 (= *exciting* ; *emotional*)。Don't be
overly *dramatic* about things. (對事情不要過份激動。)
Dreadful. 在此指 Don't be *dreadful*. (不要讓人害怕。)
Don't be a *dreadful* person to know. (不要讓認識你的人
覺得可怕。) Don't say *dreadful* things. (不要說可怕的
事。) *Dreary*. 在此指 Don't be *dreary*. (不要讓人討厭。)
(= *Don't be tedious*.) Don't have a *dreary* attitude. (不
要有讓人討厭的態度。) Avoid *dreary* subjects. (避免談論
讓人討厭的話題。)(= *Avoid talking about dreary subjects*.)
dreary 的主要意思是「天氣陰沈的」,可引申為「無聊的;
乏味的;討人厭的;讓人討厭的」。

II. 英語演講：

【一字英語演講】

Boys and girls, ladies and gentlemen:

Don't be defensive.
Desperate.
Destructive.

Difficult.
Dishonest.
Disgraceful.

Dramatic.
Dreadful.
Dreary.

I mean this from the bottom of my heart.

【短篇英語演講】

Boys and girls, ladies and gentlemen:
各位男孩和女孩，各位先生和女士：

Don't be a *defensive* person. 不要被激怒。
Don't be *desperate*. 不要絕望。
Don't be a *destructive* person. 不要搞破壞。

Don't be *difficult* to deal with. 不要難相處。
Don't be a *dishonest* person. 不要不誠實。
Don't be *disgraceful*. 不要丟臉。

Don't be overly *dramatic* about things.
對事情不要過份激動。
Don't be a *dreadful* person to know.
不要讓認識你的人覺得可怕。
Don't be *dreary*. 不要讓人討厭。

I mean this from the bottom of my heart.
我這麼說是發自內心，非常認真的。

III. 短篇作文：

Heartfelt Advice

My advice is simple and heartfelt. *To begin with*, don't get *defensive* when someone points out your mistake. If you're a hopeless type of character, people will know you are *desperate*. *Likewise*, don't make things worse for yourself by developing *destructive* habits. *Meanwhile*, don't be a *difficult* person. Don't be *dishonest* with others. Avoid *disgraceful* habits. *Moreover*, don't be a *dramatic* person who says *dreadful* things. *And* please avoid talking about *dreary* subjects.

衷心的建議

我的建議很簡單,而且是真心的。首先,當有人指出你的錯誤時,不要被激怒。如果你是那種不抱希望的人,大家會知道你很絕望。同樣地,不要養成破壞性的習慣,使自己的情況更糟。同時,不要做個難相處的人。不要對別人不誠實。不要有丟人的習性。此外,不要太激動,說出可怕的事。而且請你要避免談論讓人討厭的話題。

* heartfelt〔ˈhɑrtˌfɛlt〕*adj.* 衷心的

IV. 填空:

D

First of all, don't be a ___1___ person who can't take criticism. Don't be a ___2___ character. Don't be a ___3___ person.

In the same manner, don't be ___4___ to deal with. Don't be a ___5___ person who lies, cheats, and steals. Don't do or say ___6___ things.

Furthermore, don't be overly ___7___ about things. Don't be a ___8___ person. And last but not least, don't be a ___9___ person to know.

首先,不要做一個無法接受批評,容易被激怒的人。不要做一個絕望的人。不要搞破壞。

同樣地,不要難相處。不要做一個會說謊、欺騙,和偷竊的不誠實的人。不要做或說丟臉的事。

此外,對事情不要過份激動。不要做一個可怕的人。最後一項要點是,不要讓認識你的人覺得討厭。

【解答】 1. defensive　2. desperate　3. destructive
4. difficult　5. dishonest　6. disgraceful
7. dramatic　8. dreadful　9. dreary

* criticism〔ˈkrɪtəˌsɪzəm〕*n.* 批評
manner〔ˈmænɚ〕*n.* 方式;樣子　*in the same manner* 同樣地
deal with 應付;打交道　*last but not least* 最後一項要點是

V. 詞彙題：

Directions: *Choose the one word that best completes the sentence.*

1. Avoid getting _____ about making a mistake.
   (A) definite (B) delightful (C) deliberate (D) defensive

2. Don't wait until you're _____ to make a change in your life.
   (A) desperate (B) dual (C) democratic (D) dense

3. _____ behavior leads to one place: an early grave.
   (A) Deputy (B) Destined (C) Destructive (D) Descriptive

4. If you have a reputation for being _____, no one will hire you.
   (A) digital (B) difficult (C) diligent (D) decisive

5. Be as _____ as you want, but the truth will come out.
   (A) dusty (B) dominant (C) dishonest (D) dependent

6. Your _____ behavior will bring shame upon the family.
   (A) distant (B) durable (C) dynamic (D) disgraceful

7. _____ outbursts will attract the wrong kind of attention.
   (A) Divine (B) Dramatic (C) Dizzy (D) Domestic

8. There has been a _____ earthquake in Iran.
   (A) dreadful (B) dental (C) dubious (D) decent

9. There's nothing worse than having to deal with a _____ person.
   (A) desirable (B) diverse (C) dreary (D) domestic

【答案】 1.(D) 2.(A) 3.(C) 4.(B) 5.(C) 6.(D)
　　　　 7.(B) 8.(A) 9.(C)

VI. 同義字整理：

1. **defensive** 〔 dɪ'fɛnsɪv 〕 *adj.*
   防禦的；惱怒的
   - = protective 〔 prə'tɛktɪv 〕
   - = irritated 〔'ɪrə,tetɪd 〕
   - = oversensitive 〔'ovə·'sɛnsətɪv 〕
   - = easily offended

2. **desperate** 〔'dɛspərɪt 〕 *adj.*
   絕望的
   - = hopeless 〔'hoplɪs 〕
   - = in despair
   - = severe 〔 sə'vɪr 〕
   - = extreme 〔 ɪk'strim 〕

3. **destructive** 〔 dɪ'strʌktɪv 〕 *adj.*
   破壞性的
   - = hurtful 〔'hɝtfəl 〕
   - = harmful 〔'hɑrmfəl 〕
   - = damaging 〔'dæmɪdʒɪŋ 〕
   - = undermining 〔,ʌndə·'maɪnɪŋ 〕

4. **difficult** 〔'dɪfə,kʌlt 〕 *adj.*
   困難的；難相處的
   - = stubborn 〔'stʌbə·n 〕
   - = demanding 〔 dɪ'mændɪŋ 〕
   - = troublesome 〔'trʌbl̩səm 〕
   - = hard to please

5. **dishonest** 〔 dɪs'ɑnɪst 〕 *adj.*
   不誠實的
   - = lying 〔'laɪɪŋ 〕
   - = cheating 〔'tʃitɪŋ 〕
   - = deceitful 〔 dɪ'sitfəl 〕
   - = deceptive 〔 dɪ'sɛptɪv 〕

6. **disgraceful** 〔 dɪs'gresfəl 〕 *adj.*
   可恥的
   - = shameful 〔'ʃemfəl 〕
   - = infamous 〔'ɪnfəməs 〕
   - = degrading 〔 dɪ'gredɪŋ 〕
   - = disreputable 〔 dɪs'rɛpjətəbl̩ 〕
   - = dishonorable 〔 dɪs'ɑnərəbl̩ 〕

7. **dramatic** 〔 drə'mætɪk 〕 *adj.*
   戲劇性的
   - = emotional 〔 ɪ'moʃənl̩ 〕
   - = sensational 〔 sɛn'seʃənl̩ 〕

8. **dreadful** 〔'drɛdfəl 〕 *adj.* 可怕的
   - = awful 〔'ɔfl̩ 〕
   - = terrible 〔'tɛrəbl̩ 〕
   - = horrible 〔'hɑrəbl̩ 〕

9. **dreary** 〔'drɪrɪ 〕 *adj.* 討人厭的；
   無聊的
   - = dull 〔 dʌl 〕
   - = boring 〔'borɪŋ 〕
   - = tedious 〔'tidɪəs 〕

D

Good Advice: What Not to Do

7. E

看英文唸出中文	一口氣說九句		看中文唸出英文

exclude[5]

〔 ɪkˋsklud 〕 *v.*

exploit[6]

〔 ɪkˋsplɔɪt 〕 *v.*

exaggerate[4]

〔 ɪgˋzædʒə͵ret 〕 *v.*

字首是 ex

Don't exclude others. 不要排除他人。

Exploit others. 不要利用他人。

Exaggerate. 不要誇大。

都有 others

排除

利用

誇大

---

envy[3]

〔 ˋɛnvɪ 〕 *v. n.*

endanger[4]

〔 ɪnˋdendʒɚ 〕 *v.*

embarrass[4]

〔 ɪmˋbærəs 〕 *v.*

字首是 En

Envy others. 不要羨慕他人。

Endanger others. 不要危害他人。

Embarrass others. 不要讓人尷尬。

都有 others

羨慕

危害

使尷尬

---

evil[3]

〔 ˋivḷ 〕 *adj.*

extreme[3]

〔 ɪkˋstrim 〕 *adj.*

emotional[4]

〔 ɪˋmoʃənḷ 〕 *adj.*

句意相關

Don't be evil. 不要做壞人。

Extreme. 不要走極端。

Emotional. 不要情緒化。

邪惡的

極端的

情緒化的

I. 背景說明：

Don't exclude others. 如果你和兩個人在說話的時候，不要排除其中一人，只跟一個人說。(*If you're having a conversation with two people, don't exclude one person by speaking to only the other person.*) Don't *exclude* yourself from social activities. (不要不參加社交活動。) *Don't exclude others* from your life. (在你的生活中不要排除別人。) *Exploit others.* 在此指 Don't *exploit others.* (不要利用他人。) Don't *exploit* or abuse *others.* (不要利用或虐待他人。) Don't *exploit* people for your benefit. (不要為了自己的利益而利用人。) (= *Don't take advantage of people.*) exploit 可作「利用」或「剝削」解。*Exaggerate.* 在此指 Don't *exaggerate.* (不要誇大。) (= *Don't talk big.*) Don't boast or *exaggerate.* (不要吹牛或誇大。) Don't be a person who *exaggerates.* (不要做一個誇大的人。)

　　Envy others. 在此指 Don't *envy others.* (不要羨慕別人。) 可說成：Don't *envy* what *others* have. (不要羨慕別人擁有的東西。) Learn the difference between jealousy and *envy.* (要知道嫉妒和羨慕之間的不同。) *Endanger others.* 在此指 Don't *endanger others.* (不要危害別人。) (= *Don't put others in a position to be harmed.*) 不可只說 Don't *endanger.* (誤)，句意不全。Don't carelessly *endanger others.* (不要不小心危害到別人。) Don't do anything to *endanger* yourself. (不要做任何會危害自己的事。)

Embarrass others. 在此指 Don't *embarrass others*. (不要讓
人尷尬。) Don't *embarrass* yourself. (不要使自己難堪。)
Don't *embarrass* your family and friends. (不要讓你的家人
和朋友難堪。)

    Don't be *evil*. (不要做壞人。) (= *Don't be an evil person.*)
Don't think *evil* thoughts. (不要有邪惡的想法。) Don't do
evil deeds. (不要做壞事。) (= *Don't do bad things.*) *Extreme*.
在此指 Don't be *extreme*. (不要走極端。) (= *Don't be an
extreme person.*) Avoid being *extreme*. (避免走極端。)
Emotional. 在此指 Don't be *emotional*. (不要情緒化。)
Don't be an *emotional* person. (不要做一個情緒化的人。)
Don't be too *emotional*. (不要太情緒化。)

Dear friends and associates:

Don't exclude others.
Exploit others.
Exaggerate.

Envy others.
Endanger others.
Embarrass others.

Don't be evil.
Extreme.
Emotional.

***These are all things to avoid
in the future.***

II. 短篇英語演講：

Dear friends and associates: 親愛的朋友和同事：

Don't exclude others. 不要排除他人。
Don't **exploit others** to your benefit.
不要為了自己的利益而利用他人。
Don't be a person who **exaggerates**. 不要做一個誇大的人。

Don't **envy** what **others** have. 不要羨慕別人擁有的東西。
Don't carelessly **endanger others**. 不要不小心危害到別人。
Don't **embarrass others**. 不要讓人尷尬。

Don't be an **evil** person. 不要做壞人。
Don't be an **extreme** person. 不要走極端。
Don't be too **emotional**. 不要太情緒化。

These are all things to avoid in the future.
這些都是未來要避免的事。

III. 短篇作文：

Things to Avoid

Avoid these things. *First*, if you're talking to more than one person, don't *exclude* anybody from the conversation. Don't *exploit* or abuse *others*. Don't boast or *exaggerate*. *Additionally*, learn the difference between jealousy and *envy*. Don't put others in a position to be harmed. Don't do anything to *endanger* yourself. *On top of that*, don't *embarrass* your family and friends. *Don't be* an *evil* person. Avoid being *extreme*. *And finally*, avoid being an *emotional* person in the future.

要避免的事

　　要避免以下這些事。首先，如果你跟一個以上的人談話，不要將任何人排除在對話之外。不要利用或虐待他人。不要吹牛或誇大。而且，要知道嫉妒和羨慕之間的不同。不要危害別人。不要做任何會危害自己的事。此外，不要讓你的家人和朋友難堪。不要做壞人。避免走極端。最後，將來要避免成為一個情緒化的人。

　　* learn〔lɝn〕v. 知道　　jealousy〔'dʒɛləsɪ〕n. 嫉妒
　　put〔pʊt〕v. 使成為（某種狀態）　　position〔pə'zɪʃən〕n. 處境

IV. 填空：

　　To begin with, don't ___1___ yourself from social activities. Don't ___2___ people for your benefit. Don't be a person who ___3___.

　　In the same fashion, don't ___4___ what others have; be happy with what you have. Don't carelessly ___5___ others. Don't ___6___ yourself by doing stupid things.

　　On top of that, don't think ___7___ thoughts. Don't be an ___8___ person. And finally, avoid being too ___9___ and dramatic.

　　首先，不要不參加社交活動。不要為了自己的利益而利用人。不要做一個誇大的人。

　　同樣地，不要羨慕別人擁有的東西；要滿足於自己所擁有的。不要不小心危害到別人。不要做愚蠢的事，使自己難堪。

　　此外，不要有邪惡的想法。不要走極端。最後，不要太情緒化、太激動。

【解答】 1. exclude　2. exploit　3. exaggerates　4. envy
　　　　 5. endanger　6. embarrass　7. evil　8. extreme
　　　　 9. emotional
　　* fashion〔'fæʃən〕n. 方式；作風
　　　in the same fashion 同樣地　　happy〔'hæpɪ〕adj. 滿意的

V. 詞彙題：

Directions: Choose the one word that best completes the sentence.

1. It's very rude to purposely _____ one person from a group conversation.
   (A) excel   (B) examine   (C) exclude   (D) excite

2. There are very severe penalties for _____ others.
   (A) explaining   (B) expanding   (C) exiling   (D) exploiting

3. Those who consistently _____ are less likely to be believed.
   (A) exaggerate   (B) exchange   (C) exhibit   (D) execute

4. You won't _____ others if you're content with what you have.
   (A) enrich   (B) envy   (C) endure   (D) enforce

5. Take extra caution not to _____ yourself.
   (A) entitle   (B) endanger   (C) equate   (D) erupt

6. Don't _____ others in order to make yourself look better.
   (A) evacuate   (B) establish   (C) evolve   (D) embarrass

7. The world doesn't need more _____ people.
   (A) evident   (B) eventual   (C) evil   (D) ethnic

8. People with _____ views are dangerous, irrational, and unpredictable.
   (A) extreme   (B) equal   (C) explicit   (D) extinct

9. People with _____ problems are easily upset.
   (A) external   (B) emotional   (C) exotic   (D) eternal

【答案】 1.(C)   2.(D)   3.(A)   4.(B)   5.(B)   6.(D)
　　　　 7.(C)   8.(A)   9.(B)

VI. 同義字整理：

1. **exclude** 〔 ɪk'sklud 〕 v. 排除
   - = reject 〔 rɪ'dʒɛkt 〕
   - = keep out
   - = shut out
   - = leave out

2. **exploit** 〔 ɪk'splɔɪt 〕 v. 利用；剝削
   - = abuse 〔 ə'bjuz 〕
   - = manipulate 〔 mə'nɪpjə,let 〕
   - = take advantage of

3. **exaggerate** 〔 ɪg'zædʒə,ret 〕 v. 誇大
   - = inflate 〔 ɪn'flet 〕
   - = overstate 〔 'ovə'stet 〕
   - = overestimate 〔 ,ovə'ɛstə,met 〕
   - = overemphasize
     〔 ,ovə'ɛmfə,saɪz 〕

4. **envy** 〔 'ɛnvɪ 〕 v. n. 羨慕
   - = desire 〔 dɪ'zaɪr 〕
   - = covet 〔 'kʌvɪt 〕
   - = crave 〔 krev 〕

   - = aspire to
   - = yearn for

5. **endanger** 〔 ɪn'dendʒə 〕 v. 危害
   - = jeopardize 〔 'dʒɛpə-d,aɪz 〕
   - = put at risk
   - = put in danger

6. **embarrass** 〔 ɪm'bærəs 〕 v. 使尷尬
   - = shame 〔 ʃem 〕
   - = humiliate 〔 hju'mɪlɪ,et 〕
   - = make awkward
   - = make uncomfortable

7. **evil** 〔 'ivl̩ 〕 adj. 邪惡的
   - = wicked 〔 'wɪkɪd 〕
   - = immoral 〔 ɪ'mɔrəl 〕
   - = vicious 〔 'vɪʃəs 〕
   - = malicious 〔 mə'lɪʃəs 〕

8. **extreme** 〔 ɪk'strim 〕 adj. 極端的
   - = intense 〔 ɪn'tɛns 〕
   - = drastic 〔 'dræstɪk 〕
   - = excessive 〔 ɪk'sɛsɪv 〕

   - = unreasonable
     〔 ʌn'riznəbl̩ 〕
   - = uncompromising
     〔 ʌn'kɑmprə,maɪzɪŋ 〕

9. **emotional** 〔 ɪ'moʃənl̩ 〕 adj. 情緒化的
   - = sentimental 〔 ,sɛntə'mɛntl̩ 〕
   - = susceptible 〔 sə'sɛptəbl̩ 〕
   - = excitable 〔 ɪk'saɪtəbl̩ 〕
   - = sensitive 〔 'sɛnsətɪv 〕

Good Advice: What Not to Do

8. F (1)

看英文唸出中文	一口氣説九句	看中文唸出英文

fight[1]
〔 faɪt 〕 v.

Don't *fight*.
不要吵架。

打架；吵架

falter[5]
〔 'fɔltɚ 〕 v.

Falter.
不要猶豫。

字尾是 ter

搖晃；
猶豫

flatter[4]
〔 'flætɚ 〕 v.

Flatter.
不要奉承。

奉承

- - -

feeble[5]
〔 'fibḷ 〕 adj.

Don't be *feeble*.
不要軟弱。

三個是同義字

虛弱的

frail[6]
〔 frel 〕 adj.

Frail.
不要虛弱。

字首是 Fra

虛弱的

fragile[6]
〔 'frædʒaɪl ,
'frædʒəl 〕 adj.

Fragile.
不要脆弱。

脆弱的；易碎的

- - -

forgetful[5]
〔 fɚ'gɛtfəl 〕 adj.

Forgetful.
不要健忘。

健忘的

furious[4]
〔 'fjʊrɪəs 〕 adj.

Furious.
不要生氣。

是同義字

狂怒的

frantic[5]
〔 'fræntɪk 〕 adj.

Frantic.
不要發狂。

發狂的

F

I. 背景說明：

　　Don't fight. 中的 fight，主要的意思是「打架」，也可作「吵架」解。這句話的意思是①不要打架。(= *Don't use violence.*)②不要吵架。(= *Don't argue.*) 當然「吵架」用得比較多。Don't *fight* authority. (不要和上級對抗；民不與官鬥。) Don't *fight* your friends. (不要和朋友吵架。) (= *Don't fight with your friends.*) 學文法的人老是想到及物或不及物動詞，害死人了。動詞及物或不及物，完全依句意，背短句是最簡單的方法。*Falter*. 在此指 Don't *falter*. (不要猶豫不決。) (= *Don't hesitate.*) falter 主要的意思是「蹣跚；搖晃」，在這裡是作「猶豫；動搖；結巴」解。Don't *falter* to achieve. (不要猶豫不決，要去達成目標。) Don't *falter* in your commitment. (對你的承諾不要動搖。) Don't *falter* during a speech. (說話不要結結巴巴。) (= *Don't hesitate when you speak.*) *Flatter*. 在此指 Don't *flatter*. (不要奉承。) Don't *flatter* people. (不要奉承別人。) Don't *flatter* yourself. (不要自以爲了不起；別自以爲是。)【慣用句】

Don't falter.

Will you go out with me?
(妳願意和我出去嗎？)

I'm flattered, but I have a boyfriend.
(我受寵若驚，但我已經有男朋友了。)

Don't be feeble. 可說成：**Don't be feeble**-minded.（不要意志不堅。）(= *Don't be weak-minded.*) **Don't be feeble** and timid.（不要軟弱膽小。）**Don't be** too **feeble**.（不要太軟弱。）Don't let yourself become **feeble**.（不要使自己變得軟弱。）*Frail.* 在此指 Don't be **frail**.（不要虛弱。）(= *Don't be a frail person.*) Don't be weak and **frail**.（不要太虛弱。）*Fragile.* 在此指 Don't be **fragile**.（不要脆弱。）(= *Don't be a fragile person.*) Don't have a **fragile** ego.（不要有脆弱的自尊。）(= *Don't be too sensitive and easily offended.*) This is **fragile**, so handle it with care.（這很脆弱，所以要小心處理。）

Forgetful. 在此指 Don't be **forgetful**.（不要健忘。）Don't be a **forgetful** person.（不要做一個健忘的人。）Avoid being **forgetful**.（要避免健忘。）*Furious.* 在此指 Don't be **furious**.（不要生氣。）(= *Don't get mad.*) Don't get **furious** at mistakes.（犯錯時不要生氣。）Don't have a **furious** temper.（不要有火爆的脾氣。）*Frantic.* 在此指 Don't be **frantic**.（不要發狂。）(= *Don't be a frantic person.*) Don't be **frantic** and anxious.（不要發狂又焦慮。）(= *Don't be highly excited and nervous.*) Don't have a **frantic** personality.（不要有發狂的個性。）

II. 英語演講：

【一字英語演講】

Ladies and gentlemen, your attention, please:

Don't fight.
Falter.
Flatter.

Don't be feeble.
Frail.
Fragile.

Forgetful.
Furious.
Frantic.

These "F" words are good to know.

【短篇英語演講】

Ladies and gentlemen, your attention, please:
各位先生，各位女士，請注意：

Don't fight with your friends.
不要和你的朋友吵架。

Don't *falter* during a speech.
說話不要結結巴巴。

Don't *flatter* yourself. 不要自以爲了不起。

Don't be feeble and timid. 不要軟弱膽小。

Don't be weak and *frail.* 不要太虛弱。

Don't be a *fragile* person. 不要脆弱。

Don't be a *forgetful* person.
不要做一個健忘的人。

Don't have a *furious* temper. 不要有火爆的脾氣。

Don't be *frantic* and anxious. 不要發狂又焦慮。

These "F" words are good to know.
這些 F 開頭的字最好要知道。

III. 短篇作文：

Good "F" Words to Know

The following are some really good words that begin with "f" that you should know. *For starters*, *don't fight* with your friends. Don't *falter* in your commitment. Don't *flatter* yourself. *What's more*, don't let yourself become *feeble*. Don't be a *frail* person. Don't have a *fragile* ego. *Indeed*, avoid being *forgetful*. Don't get *furious* at mistakes. *And finally*, don't have a *frantic* personality. These are good "F" words to know.

最好要知道的 F 開頭的字

以下是一些眞的會有幫助，你應該知道的一些 f 開頭的字。首先，不要和你的朋友吵架。對你的承諾不要動搖。不要自以爲了不起。此外，不要使自己變得軟弱。不要虛弱。不要有脆弱的自尊。的確，要避免健忘。犯錯時不要生氣。最後，不要有瘋狂的個性。這些都是最好要知道的 F 開頭的字。

for starters 首先　　commitment〔kəˋmɪtmənt〕 *n.* 承諾
ego〔ˋigo〕 *n.* 自我；自尊心

IV. 填空：

To begin with, don't ___1___ with your friends. Don't ___2___ during a speech. Don't ___3___ yourself; there's always somebody better than you.

Likewise, don't be ___4___ and timid. Don't be weak and ___5___. Don't have a ___6___ ego.

Moreover, don't be a ___7___ person who can't remember details. Don't have a ___8___ temper. *Finally*, don't be ___9___ and anxious.

首先，不要和你的朋友吵架。說話不要結結巴巴。不要自以爲了不起；總是會有人比你更好。

同樣地，不要軟弱膽小。不要太虛弱。不要有脆弱的自尊。

此外，不要做一個無法記住細節，健忘的人。不要有火爆的脾氣。最後，不要發狂又焦慮。

【解答】 1. fight　 2. falter　 3. flatter　 4. feeble　 5. frail
　　　　 6. fragile　 7. forgetful　 8. furious　 9. frantic

*　timid〔ˋtɪmɪd〕 *adj.* 膽小的　　detail〔ˋditel〕 *n.* 細節
　temper〔ˋtɛmpə〕 *n.* 脾氣　　anxious〔ˋæŋkʃəs〕 *adj.* 焦慮的

V. 詞彙題：

Directions: Choose the one word that best completes the sentence.

1. Be a peaceful person and don't _____ with your friends.
   (A) fight   (B) forecast   (C) forgive   (D) fulfill

2. Practice and prepare so that you never _____.
   (A) foresee   (B) falter   (C) forbid   (D) flick

3. I'm automatically suspicious of someone who _____ me too much.
   (A) filters   (B) fades   (C) faints   (D) flatters

4. People with _____ minds are easily manipulated.
   (A) fierce   (B) feeble   (C) fluent   (D) formal

5. A _____ person can't be trusted to provide assistance.
   (A) foster   (B) frank   (C) frail   (D) forthcoming

6. A _____ ego is easily bruised.
   (A) full   (B) fresh   (C) fragile   (D) foreign

7. A _____ person is undependable.
   (A) feasible   (B) forgetful   (C) favorable   (D) flat

8. Nobody wants to deal with a _____ temper.
   (A) fair   (B) foggy   (C) fluid   (D) furious

9. We avoid people who become _____ under stress.
   (A) frantic   (B) functional   (C) following   (D) flexible

【答案】 1.（A）　2.（B）　3.（D）　4.（B）　5.（C）　6.（C）
　　　　 7.（B）　8.（D）　9.（A）

VI. 同義字整理：

1. fight 〔 faɪt 〕 *v.* 打架；吵架
- = argue 〔 ˋɑrgju 〕
- = dispute 〔 dɪˋspjut 〕
- = quarrel 〔 ˋkwɔrəl 〕
- = clash 〔 klæʃ 〕

2. falter 〔 ˋfɔltɚ 〕 *v.* 搖晃；猶豫
- = hesitate 〔 ˋhɛzəˏtet 〕
- = delay 〔 dɪˋle 〕
- = pause 〔 pɔz 〕

3. flatter 〔 ˋflætɚ 〕 *v.* 奉承
- = praise 〔 prez 〕
- = compliment 〔 ˋkɑmpləˏmɛnt 〕
- = sweet-talk 〔 ˋswitˏtɔk 〕

4. feeble 〔 ˋfibḷ 〕 *adj.* 虛弱的
- = weak 〔 wik 〕
- = frail 〔 frel 〕
- = delicate 〔 ˋdɛləkɪt 〕

5. frail 〔 frel 〕 *adj.* 虛弱的
- = weak 〔 wik 〕
- = feeble 〔 ˋfibḷ 〕
- = delicate 〔 ˋdɛləkɪt 〕
- = fragile 〔 ˋfrædʒaɪl , ˋfrædʒəl 〕
- = vulnerable 〔 ˋvʌlnərəbḷ 〕

6. fragile 〔 ˋfrædʒəl 〕 *adj.* 脆弱的；易碎的
- = weak 〔 wik 〕
- = frail 〔 frel 〕
- = feeble 〔 ˋfibḷ 〕
- = delicate 〔 ˋdɛləkɪt 〕
- = vulnerable 〔 ˋvʌlnərəbḷ 〕
- = easily broken

7. forgetful 〔 fɚˋgɛtfəl 〕 *adj.* 健忘的
- = careless 〔 ˋkɛrlɪs 〕
- = neglectful 〔 nɪˋglɛktfəl 〕
- = inattentive 〔 ˏɪnəˋtɛntɪv 〕
- = absent-minded 〔 ˋæbsṇtˋmaɪndɪd 〕

8. furious 〔 ˋfjʊrɪəs 〕 *adj.* 狂怒的
- = angry 〔 ˋæŋgrɪ 〕
- = mad 〔 mæd 〕
- = raging 〔 ˋredʒɪŋ 〕
- = enraged 〔 ɪnˋredʒd 〕

9. frantic 〔 ˋfræntɪk 〕 *adj.* 發狂的
- = mad 〔 mæd 〕
- = wild 〔 waɪld 〕
- = frenzied 〔 ˋfrɛnzɪd 〕
- = furious 〔 ˋfjʊrɪəs 〕

Good Advice: What Not to Do

9. F (2)

看英文唸出中文	一口氣說九句	看中文唸出英文
fail[2] 〔fel〕v.	Don't *fail*. 不要失敗。	失敗
fear[1] 〔fɪr〕v.	*Fear*. 不要害怕。	害怕
forsake[6] 〔fɚ'sek〕v.	*Forsake* others. 不要拋棄別人。	拋棄

		字首是 fa		
fake[3] 〔fek〕adj.		Don't be *fake*. 不要虛情假意。		假的
false[1] 〔fɔls〕adj.		*False*. 不要虛假。		假的
foolish[2] 〔'fulɪʃ〕adj.		*Foolish*. 不要愚蠢。		愚蠢的

字首是 Fo

---

foul[5] 〔faʊl〕adj.	*Foul*. 不要讓人討厭。	討厭的
frustrated[3] 〔'frʌstretɪd〕adj.	*Frustrated*. 不要洩氣。	洩氣的
freak[6] 〔frik〕n.	A *freak*. 不要當個怪人。	怪人

字首是 fr

F

I. 背景說明：

Don't fail. 可說成：Try not to *fail*. (儘量不要失敗。) Understand that you will probable *fail* many times. (要明白你可能會失敗很多次。) *Fear.* 在此指 Don't *fear*. (不要害怕。) (= *Don't be afraid.*) Don't *fear* change. (不要害怕改變。) Don't *fear* challenges. (不要害怕挑戰。) 不可說成：*Don't fear to accept a challenge.* (誤) 但可說成：Don't be afraid to accept a challenge. (不要害怕接受挑戰。) 用文法造句非常危險，規則無限多，例外無限多，背短句是最好的方法。 *Forsake others.* 在此指 Don't *forsake others*. (不要拋棄別人。) Don't *forsake* your friends. (不要拋棄你的朋友。) Don't *forsake* your family. (不要拋棄你的家人。)

Fake. 在此指 Don't be *fake*. (不要虛情假意。) (= *Don't be a fake person.*) Don't have a *fake* personality. (不要有虛假的個性。) *False.* 在此指 Don't be *false*. (不要虛假。) Don't make a *false* statement. (不要說假話。) Don't be a *false* person. (不要做一個虛情假意的人。) *Foolish.* 在此指 Don't be *foolish*. (不要愚蠢。) (= *Don't be a foolish person.*) Don't act *foolishly*. (行為舉止不要愚蠢。) 所謂 foolish，就是「不聰明的」(= *unwise*)、「不理智的」(= *unreasonable*)。

Don't be fake.

F

Foul. 在此指 Don't be *foul.*（不要讓人討厭。）(= *Don't be a foul person.*) foul 的意思有：①骯髒的 (= *dirty*) ②犯規的 (= *not allowed by rules*) ③煩躁的 (= *angry*) ④（天氣）惡劣的⑤討厭的 (= *unpleasant*)；邪惡的 (= *evil*)。Don't use *foul* language.（不要說髒話。）不可說成：*Don't speak foul language.*（誤）可說：Don't speak of *foul* things.（不要說髒話。）*Frustrated.* 在此指 Don't be *frustrated.*（不要洩氣。）(= *Don't be discouraged.*) Don't let yourself be *frustrated.*（不要讓自己洩氣。）Don't get easily *frustrated.*（不要容易洩氣。）frustrated 的意思有：「受挫的；懊惱的；失望的；沮喪的；挫敗的；失意的；洩氣的」。動詞是 frustrate（挫敗；使受挫折；使煩惱；使灰心；使沮喪）。The pay is so little, it *frustrates* me.（薪水太少了，使我很灰心。）I'm *frustrated* when you ignore me.（你不理我的時候，我很難過。）Why are you so *frustrated*?（你為什麼那麼沮喪？）*A freak.* 在此指 Don't be *a freak.*（不要當一個怪人。）Don't associate with *freaks.*（不要和怪人來往。）(= *Don't deal with freaks.*)【associate〔əˋsoʃɪͺet〕v. 交往】Don't let yourself become *a freak.*（不要讓自己變成一個怪人。）freak 的同義字是 odd person（奇怪的人）和 abnormal person（不正常的人）。

II. 英語演講：

【一字英語演講】

Students, parents, and teachers:

Don't fail.
Fear.
Forsake others.

Don't be fake.
False.
Foolish.

Foul.
Frustrated.
A freak.

Do this and you'll go far in life.

【短篇英語演講】

Students, parents, and teachers:
各位同學、家長，和老師：

Don't be afraid to *fail.* 不要害怕失敗。
Don't *fear* change. 不要害怕改變。
Don't *forsake others.* 不要拋棄別人。

Don't be a *fake* person. 不要虛情假意。
Don't be a *false* person.
不要做一個虛情假意的人。
Don't act *foolishly.* 行為舉止不要愚蠢。

Don't be a *foul* person. 不要讓人討厭。
Don't let yourself be *frustrated.* 不要讓自己洩氣。
Don't associate with *freaks.* 不要和怪人來往。

Do this and you'll go far in life.
這麼做，你的人生就會成功。

F

III. 短篇作文：

How to Go Far in Life

In order to go far in life, you have to understand that you will probably *fail* many times. *Meanwhile, fear* is your enemy. Don't *fear* change and don't be afraid to accept a challenge. *Likewise,* don't *forsake* your family. Don't have a *fake* personality. Don't make *false* statements. *On top of that,* don't be a *foolish* person. Don't use *foul* language—it makes you sound uneducated. *And* don't get easily *frustrated.* *At the end of the day,* if you don't let yourself become *a freak,* you'll go far in life.

如何擁有成功的人生

　　爲了要有成功的人生，你必須了解，你可能會失敗很多次。同時，恐懼是你的敵人。不要害怕改變，也不要害怕接受挑戰。同樣地，不要拋棄你的家人。不要有虛假的個性。不要說假話。此外，不要做一個愚蠢的人。不要說髒話——這會使你聽起來像是沒受過教育。而且不要很容易就洩氣。最後，如果你不讓自己成爲怪人，你的人生就會成功。

> * *go far* 成功　　statement (ˈstetmənt) *n.* 敘述；說明
> *at the end of the day* 總之；最後

IV. 填空：

　　For sure, a person who is not afraid to ___1___ will go far in life. Don't ___2___ change. Don't ___3___ your friends and family.

　　Consequently, don't be a ___4___ person who nobody can trust. Don't be a ___5___ person with malicious intentions. Don't act ___6___.

　　Finally, don't be a ___7___ person. Don't let yourself be ___8___ by setbacks. Don't associate with ___9___ and you'll go far in life.

　　的確，不怕失敗的人，就會有成功的人生。不要害怕改變。不要拋棄你的朋友和家人。

　　因此，不要做一個沒有人能信任，虛情假意的人。不要做一個心懷惡意，虛情假意的人。行爲舉止不要愚蠢。

　　最後，不要讓人討厭。不要讓自己因爲挫折而洩氣。不要和怪人來往，你才能擁有成功的人生。

【解答】1. fail　2. fear　3. forsake　4. fake　5. false
　　　　6. foolishly　7. foul　8. frustrated　9. freaks

> * *for sure* 確實地　　malicious (məˈlɪʃəs) *adj.* 惡意的
> intention (ɪnˈtɛnʃən) *n.* 意圖
> act (ækt) *v.* 行爲舉止；表現　　setback (ˈsɛtˌbæk) *n.* 挫折

V. 詞彙題：

Directions: Choose the one word that best completes the sentence.

1. You only _____ when you stop trying.
   (A) flap   (B) flourish   (C) fail   (D) forbid

2. People may _____ a brutal leader, but they don't respect him.
   (A) fold   (B) fetch   (C) faint   (D) fear

3. There is no greater shame than _____ one's family.
   (A) fascinating   (B) forsaking   (C) facilitating
   (D) featuring

4. People can easily see through a _____ personality.
   (A) fertile   (B) federal   (C) fake   (D) finite

5. Avoid making _____ statements.
   (A) false   (B) fireproof   (C) fragrant   (D) forgetful

6. There's no way to help a person who makes _____ decisions.
   (A) fortunate   (B) friendly   (C) faithful   (D) foolish

7. Keep your distance from people with _____ personalities.
   (A) foul   (B) famous   (C) further   (D) frequent

8. Everybody gets _____ from time to time, so don't let it bother you.
   (A) fortified   (B) focused   (C) frustrated   (D) fastened

9. Nobody wants to be thought of as a _____.
   (A) fan   (B) freak   (C) fever   (D) fiddle

【答案】 1.(C) 2.(D) 3.(B) 4.(C) 5.(A) 6.(D)
        7.(A) 8.(C) 9.(B)

VI. 同義字整理：

1. **fail**〔 fel 〕 *v.* 失敗
   - = fall short
   - = not pass
   - = be defeated
   - = be unsuccessful

2. **fear** 〔 fɪr 〕 *v.* 害怕
   - = be afraid of
   - = be scared of
   - = be terrified by
   - = be frightened of

3. **forsake** 〔 fə'sek 〕 *v.* 拋棄
   - = desert 〔 dɪ'zɜt 〕
   - = abandon 〔 ə'bændən 〕
   - = leave 〔 liv 〕
   - = give up

4. **fake** 〔 fek 〕 *adj.* 假的
   - = false 〔 fɔls 〕
   - = forged 〔 fɔrdʒd 〕
   - = assumed 〔 ə'sjumd 〕
   - = counterfeit 〔'kaʊntəfɪt 〕

5. **false** 〔 fɔls 〕 *adj.* 假的
   - = fake 〔 fek 〕
   - = untruthful 〔 ʌn'truθfəl 〕
   - = counterfeit 〔'kaʊntəfɪt 〕
   - = dishonest 〔 dɪs'ɑnɪst 〕
   - = insincere 〔ˌɪnsɪn'sɪr 〕

6. **foolish** 〔'fulɪʃ 〕 *adj.* 愚蠢的
   - = dumb 〔 dʌm 〕
   - = stupid 〔'stjupɪd 〕
   - = unwise 〔 ʌn'waɪz 〕
   - = indiscreet 〔ˌɪndɪ'skrit 〕

7. **foul** 〔 faʊl 〕 *adj.* 討厭的
   - = nasty 〔'næstɪ 〕
   - = vulgar 〔'vʌlgə 〕
   - = indecent 〔 ɪn'disn̩t 〕
   - = offensive 〔 ə'fɛnsɪv 〕
   - = unpleasant 〔 ʌn'plɛzn̩t 〕

8. **frustrated** 〔'frʌstretɪd 〕 *adj.* 洩氣的
   - = disappointed 〔ˌdɪsə'pɔɪntɪd 〕
   - = discouraged 〔 dɪs'kɜɪdʒd 〕
   - = disheartened 〔 dɪs'hartn̩d 〕

9. **freak** 〔 frik 〕 *n.* 怪人
   - = weirdo 〔'wɪrdo 〕
   - = eccentric 〔 ɪk'sɛntrɪk 〕
   - = oddity 〔'ɑdətɪ 〕

Good Advice: What Not to Do

10. G

看英文唸出中文	一口氣說九句	看中文唸出英文
groan 5 〔gron〕v.	字首都是 gr，是擬聲字	Don't *groan*. 不要嘀咕抱怨。	呻吟
grumble 5 〔'grʌmbl̩〕v.		*Grumble*. 不要抱怨。	抱怨
growl 5 〔graʊl〕v.		*Growl*. 不要大吼大叫。	咆哮

grieve 4 〔griv〕v.	*Grieve*. 不要傷心。	悲傷
gossip 3 〔'gɑsəp〕v.	*Gossip*. 不要說閒話。	說閒話
glare 5 〔glɛr〕v.	*Glare*. 不要瞪人家。	怒視

greedy 2 〔'gridɪ〕adj.	字首是 gr　字尾是 y	Don't be *greedy*. 不要貪心。	貪心的
grim 5 〔grɪm〕adj.		*Grim*. 不要太嚴肅。	嚴肅的
gloomy 6 〔'glumɪ〕adj.		*Gloomy*. 不要悲觀。	昏暗的；悲觀的

G

I. 背景說明：

    Don't groan. 中的 groan，主要的意思是「（因痛苦或煩惱而）呻吟」，如發出 uhhh... 〔ʌ〕*interj.* 啊；嗯；唔，aww... 〔ɔ〕*interj.* 呀等聲音。

    Don't groan.（不要嘀咕抱怨。）(= *Don't express your displeasure with an inarticulate sound.*) *Don't groan* about your troubles.（不要嘀咕抱怨你的困難。）*Grumble.* 在此指 Don't *grumble.*（不要抱怨。）Don't *grumble* about life.（不要抱怨你的生活。）*Grumbling* is unattractive.（抱怨讓人討厭。）(= *Grumbling is unpleasant.*) *Growl.* 在此指 Don't *growl.*（不要咆哮。）(= *Don't speak in an angry way.*) When a dog *growls* at you, put your hands on your waist to calm it down.（當狗對你咆哮時，可以雙手插腰，狗就會停止對你咆哮。）Don't *growl* at people.（不要對人咆哮。）*Growling* at others won't solve your problem.（對他人咆哮無法解決你的問題。）

Grieve. 在此指 Don't *grieve*. (不要傷心。)(= *Don't be sad.*) Don't *grieve* about your loss. (不要為了你的損失而傷心。) Don't *grieve* about mistakes. (不要因為錯誤而傷心。)
Gossip. 在此指 Don't *gossip*. (不要說閒話。) Don't *gossip* about others. (不要說別人的閒話。) *Gossiping* is bad. (說閒話不是好事。) *Glare*. 在此指 Don't *glare*. (不要瞪人家。)(= *Don't glare at people.*) *Glaring* at people makes them uncomfortable. (瞪人家會使他們不舒服。)

Don't be greedy. (不要貪心。)(= *Don't be a greedy person.*) A *greedy* person is an ugly person. (貪心的人就是醜陋的人。) *Grim*. 在此指 Don't be *grim*. (不要太嚴肅。) Don't have a *grim* character. (不要有嚴肅的個性。) grim 的意思是「嚴肅的;冷酷的」(= *very serious and unfriendly.*) Avoid talking about *grim* subjects. (要避免談論嚴肅的話題。) *Gloomy*. 在此指 Don't be *gloomy*. (不要悲觀。)(= *Don't be pessimistic.*) Don't be a *gloomy* person. (不要做一個悲觀的人。) Nobody likes to be around a *gloomy* person. (沒有人喜歡和憂鬱的人在一起。) gloomy 的主要意思是「昏暗的」

Don't be gloomy.

(= *dark*),如 It's a *gloomy* day. (今天天色昏暗。) 在此引申為「憂鬱的;悲觀的;情緒低落的;沮喪的;憂傷的」。

II. 英語演講：

【一字英語演講】 【短篇英語演講】

Greetings, one and all:

Greetings, one and all: 大家好：

Don't groan.
Grumble.
Growl.

Don't groan about your troubles.
不要嘀咕你的困難。
Don't *grumble* about life. 不要抱怨你的生活。
Don't *growl* at people. 不要對人咆哮。

Grieve.
Gossip.
Glare.

Don't *grieve* about mistakes. 不要因為錯誤而傷心。
Don't *gossip* about others. 不要說別人的閒話。
Don't *glare* at people. 不要瞪人家。

Don't be greedy.
Grim.
Gloomy.

Don't be a *greedy* person. 不要貪心。
Don't have a *grim* character. 不要有嚴肅的個性。
Don't be a *gloomy* person. 不要做一個悲觀的人。

Try being a positive person instead.

Try being a positive person instead.
試著改做一個樂觀的人。

III. 短篇作文：

Be a Positive Person

Do you want to be a positive person? *First of all, don't groan* and complain in an inarticulate way. *Grumbling* is unattractive. Somebody who is always *growling* needs to calm down. *Meanwhile*, don't *grieve* about your loss. *Likewise, gossiping* is bad. *Glaring* at people makes them uncomfortable. A *greedy* person is an ugly person. Avoid talking about *grim* subjects. *Most importantly*, nobody likes to be around a *gloomy* person. Try being positive for a change.

做一個樂觀的人

你想要成為一個樂觀的人嗎？首先，不要含糊不清地嘀咕抱怨。抱怨讓人討厭。總是在咆哮的人需要冷靜下來。同時，不要為了你的損失而傷心。同樣地，說閒話不是好事。瞪人家會使他們不舒服。貪心的人就是醜陋的人。不要談論嚴肅的話題。最重要的是，沒有人喜歡和憂鬱的人在一起。試著樂觀一點，改變一下。

* positive〔'pɑzətɪv〕 *adj.* 樂觀的
  inarticulate〔ˌɪnɑr'tɪkjəlɪt〕 *adj.* 口齒不清的
  for a change 改變一下

IV. 填空：

Positive people never ___1___ about their troubles. Similarly, they don't ___2___ and constantly complain about life. So, don't ___3___ in an angry way.

On the other hand, don't ___4___ about mistakes. Don't ___5___ or spread rumors about others. Don't ___6___ at people in a menacing way.

Moreover, don't be a ___7___ person who is never satisfied. Don't have a ___8___ and unwelcoming character. Nobody likes a ___9___ person, so be positive.

樂觀的人從不嘀咕抱怨他們的困難。同樣地，他們不會持續抱怨自己的生活。所以，不要生氣地咆哮。

另一方面，不要因為錯誤而傷心。不要說閒話或散佈和別人有關的謠言。不要以威脅的方式瞪人家。

此外，不要做一個永遠不滿足的貪心的人。不要有嚴肅而且不友善的個性。沒有人喜歡悲觀的人，所以要樂觀一點。

【解答】 1. groan 2. grumble 3. growl 4. grieve 5. gossip
6. glare 7. greedy 8. grim 9. gloomy
* rumor〔'rumɚ〕 *n.* 謠言　　menacing〔'mɛnɪsɪŋ〕 *adj.* 威脅的

G

V. 詞彙題：

Directions: *Choose the one word that best completes the sentence.*

1. Don't let anybody hear you _____ about your problems.
   (A) grinding   (B) groaning   (C) groping   (D) growing

2. If you're going to _____ about something, do it in private.
   (A) guess   (B) guide   (C) gulp   (D) grumble

3. Nothing good will come from _____ like a dog.
   (A) grasping   (B) graduating   (C) growling   (D) governing

4. _____ is for the living, not the dead.
   (A) Gliding   (B) Glancing   (C) Grieving   (D) Glittering

5. She is always _____ with her friends about her neighbors.
   (A) gossiping   (B) gleaming   (C) gathering   (D) generating

6. _____ at someone is extremely offensive.
   (A) Glistening   (B) Glaring   (C) Governing   (D) Granting

7. A good neighbor is generous instead of _____.
   (A) grassy   (B) greasy   (C) greedy   (D) guilty

8. Nobody wants to talk about _____ subjects like death.
   (A) graphic   (B) gracious   (C) gradual   (D) grim

9. The _____ person will sit in the corner and eat lunch by himself.
   (A) gloomy   (B) grateful   (C) global   (D) genetic

【答案】 1.(B) 2.(D) 3.(C) 4.(C) 5.(A) 6.(B)
　　　 7.(C) 8.(D) 9.(A)

VI. 同義字整理：

1. groan ﹝ gron ﹞ v. 呻吟

- = complain ﹝ kəm'plen ﹞
- = grumble ﹝ 'grʌmbḷ ﹞
- = whine ﹝ hwaɪn ﹞
- = object ﹝ əb'dʒɛkt ﹞

2. grumble ﹝ 'grʌmbḷ ﹞ v. 抱怨

- = complain ﹝ kəm'plen ﹞
- = moan ﹝ mon ﹞
- = whine ﹝ hwaɪn ﹞

3. growl ﹝ graʊl ﹞ v. 咆哮

- = snarl ﹝ snɑrl ﹞
- = show your teeth

4. grieve ﹝ griv ﹞ v. 悲傷

- = mourn ﹝ morn ﹞
- = lament ﹝ lə'mɛnt ﹞
- = weep ﹝ wip ﹞
- = suffer ﹝ 'sʌfɚ ﹞

5. gossip ﹝ 'gɑsəp ﹞ v. 說閒話

- = chat ﹝ tʃæt ﹞
- = chatter ﹝ 'tʃætɚ ﹞

- = chew the fat
- = shoot the breeze
- = spread rumors

6. glare ﹝ glɛr ﹞ v. 怒視

- = scowl ﹝ skaʊl ﹞
- = stare angrily
- = give a dirty look

7. greedy ﹝ 'gridɪ ﹞ adj. 貪心的

- = desirous ﹝ dɪ'zaɪrəs ﹞
- = covetous ﹝ 'kʌvɪtəs ﹞
- = grasping ﹝ 'græspɪŋ ﹞
- = selfish ﹝ 'sɛlfɪʃ ﹞

8. grim ﹝ grɪm ﹞ adj. 嚴肅的

- = severe ﹝ sə'vɪr ﹞
- = harsh ﹝ hɑrʃ ﹞
- = grave ﹝ grev ﹞
- = solemn ﹝ 'saləm ﹞

9. gloomy ﹝ 'glumɪ ﹞ adj. 昏暗的；
悲觀的；憂鬱的

- = sad ﹝ sæd ﹞
- = down ﹝ daʊn ﹞
- = miserable ﹝ 'mɪzərəbḷ ﹞
- = melancholy ﹝ 'mɛlən͵kɑlɪ ﹞

G

Good Advice: What Not to Do

11. H

看英文唸出中文	一 口 氣 說 九 句	看中文唸出英文
hate¹ 〔 het 〕 *v.*	Don't *hate*. 不要怨恨。	恨
hurt¹ 〔 hɝt 〕 *v.*	*Hurt* others. 不要傷害別人。	傷害
hesitate³ 〔'hɛzə,tet 〕 *v.*	*Hesitate*. 不要猶豫。	猶豫

字尾是 ate

howl⁵ 〔 haʊl 〕 *v.*	*Howl*. 不要怒吼。	怒吼
harass⁶ 〔 hə'ræs 〕 *v.*	*Harass* others. 不要騷擾別人。	騷擾
humiliate⁶ 〔 hju'mɪlɪ,et 〕 *v.*	*Humiliate* others. 不要羞辱別人。	使丟臉

由短到長　都有 others

harsh⁴ 〔 hɑrʃ 〕 *adj.*	Don't be *harsh*. 不要太嚴厲。	嚴厲的
hasty³ 〔'hestɪ 〕 *adj.*	*Hasty*. 不要太草率。	匆忙的
hysterical⁶ 〔 hɪs'tɛrɪkl̩ 〕 *adj.*	*Hysterical*. 不要歇斯底里。	歇斯底里的

字首是 ha

H

I. 背景說明：

Don't hate. 可說成：*Don't hate* people.（不要怨恨別人。）*Don't hate* others without good reason.（沒有正當的理由，不要怨恨別人。）*Hurt others.* 在此指 Don't **hurt** *others.*（不要傷害別人。）(= *Don't hurt people.*) Don't **hurt** or abuse *others.*（不要傷害或虐待別人。）*Hesitate.* 在此指 Don't **hesitate.**（不要猶豫。）Don't **hesitate** to act.（要採取行動，不要猶豫。）(= *Don't hesitate to do something.*) Don't **hesitate** to speak your mind.（不要猶豫說真話。）(= *Say what is on your mind.* = *Be blunt.*)

Howl. 在此指 Don't **howl.**（不要怒吼。）(= *Don't speak in a loud angry voice.*) Don't **howl** like a wolf.（不要像狼一樣地嗥叫。）狼在夜裡叫，就是 howl。Don't **howl.** 也可翻成「不要大聲哭。」(= *Don't cry loudly.*) Don't **howl** at others.（不要對別人怒吼。）Don't **howl** and scream at people.（不要對別人怒吼尖叫。）*Harrass others.* 在此指 Don't **harass others.**（不要騷擾別人。）(= *Don't harass people.*) Don't **harass** or bully *others.*（不要騷擾或欺負別人。）*Humilate others.* 在此指 Don't **humiliate others.**（不要羞辱別人。）Don't **humiliate** or embarrass people.（不要羞辱或使人尷尬。）

H

Don't be harsh.（不要太嚴厲。）（= *Don't be harsh to people.*）可加強語氣說成：*Don't be* too *harsh.*（不要太嚴厲。）（= *Don't be so harsh.*）*Don't be harsh* or cruel.（不要嚴厲或殘忍。）*Hasty.* 在此指 Don't be *hasty.*（不要太草率。）可說成：Don't be *hasty* and careless.（不要草率又粗心大意。）Don't be *hasty* and reckless.（不要草率又魯莽。）*Hysterical.* 在此指 Don't be *hysterical.*（不要歇斯底里。）（= *Don't get hysterical.*）也就是「情緒不要過份激動。」Don't be *hysterical* and dramatic.（不要歇斯底里，情緒化。）

Dear students:

Don't hate.
Hurt others.
Hesitate.

Howl.
Harass others.
Humiliate others.

Don't be harsh.
Hasty.
Hysterical.

Take my advice and avoid these harmful behaviors.

H

II. 短篇英語演講：

Dear students: 親愛的同學：

Don't hate people. 不要怨恨別人。

Don't *hurt* or abuse *others*. 不要傷害或虐待別人。

Don't *hesitate* to act. 要採取行動，不要猶豫。

Don't *howl* like a wolf. 不要像狼一樣地嗥叫。

Don't *harass* or bully *others*. 不要騷擾或欺負別人。

Don't try to *humiliate others*. 不要想羞辱別人。

Don't be harsh or cruel. 不要嚴厲或殘忍。

Don't be *hasty* and reckless. 不要草率又魯莽。

Don't be *hysterical* and dramatic. 不要歇斯底里，情緒化。

Take my advice and avoid these harmful behaviors.
要聽從我的勸告，避免這些有害的行為。

III. 短篇作文：

Avoiding Harmful Behaviors

This advice will help you avoid some harmful behaviors.
First, don't hate others without good reason. Don't *hurt*
people. Don't *hesitate* to speak your mind. *At the same time,*
don't *howl* and scream at people. Don't *harass* people. Don't
humiliate or embarrass people. *Furthermore, don't be* too
harsh. Don't be *hasty* and careless. Don't be a *hysterical*
person. *With this in mind,* avoid these harmful behaviors and
you'll have no problems in life.

避免有害的行為

這些建議將會幫助你避免一些有害的行為。首先,沒有正當的理由,不要怨恨別人。不要傷害別人。不要猶豫說真話。同時,不要對別人怒吼尖叫。不要騷擾別人。不要羞辱或使人尷尬。此外,不要太嚴厲。不要草率又粗心大意。不要做一個歇斯底里的人。把這些牢記在心,避免這些有害的行為,那你的生活就不會有問題。

* ***speak one's mind*** 實話實說;說真話

IV. 填空:

For starters, don't ____1___ or despise people. Don't ____2___ or abuse others. However, don't ____3___ to act when the time is right.

Meanwhile, don't ____4___ like a wolf. Don't ____5___ or bully others. Don't try to ____6___ or embarrass people.

On top of that, don't be unnecessarily ____7___ or cruel. Don't be ____8___ and reckless. Most importantly, avoid being ____9___ and dramatic.

首先,不要怨恨或輕視人。不要傷害或虐待別人。然而,當時機正好時,要採取行動,不要猶豫。

同時,不要像狼一樣嗥叫。不要騷擾或欺負別人。不要想羞辱或使人尷尬。

此外,不要不必要地嚴厲或殘忍。不要草率又魯莽。最重要的是,要避免歇斯底里,情緒化。

【解答】 1. hate　2. hurt　3. hesitate　4. howl　5. harass
　　　　 6. humiliate　7. harsh　8. hasty　9. hysterical
　　* unnecessarily〔ʌnˈnɛsəˌsɛrəlɪ〕*adj.* 不必要地
　　　reckless〔ˈrɛklɪs〕*adj.* 魯莽的

V. 詞彙題：

Directions: *Choose the one word that best completes the sentence.*

1. You can dislike someone, but there's no reason to _____ another human being.
   (A) hate (B) haunt (C) hatch (D) hasten

2. You'll be severely punished for _____ others.
   (A) heightening (B) hurting (C) honking (D) hovering

3. As the saying goes, he who _____ is lost.
   (A) hesitates (B) hushes (C) highlights (D) heralds

4. _____ like a wolf is crude and uncivilized.
   (A) Healing (B) Heeding (C) Howling (D) Harnessing

5. It's against the law to _____ someone.
   (A) harvest (B) hike (C) hum (D) harass

6. Don't _____ people for your own amusement.
   (A) halt (B) hijack (C) humiliate (D) hurry

7. Think before saying something _____.
   (A) harsh (B) humble (C) heroic (D) household

8. _____ decisions are guaranteed to haunt you.
   (A) Homesick (B) Hasty (C) Honorary (D) Habitual

9. There's no reason to get _____ if something goes wrong.
   (A) hearty (B) historical (C) hospitable (D) hysterical

【答案】1.(A) 2.(B) 3.(A) 4.(C) 5.(D) 6.(C)
　　　　7.(A) 8.(B) 9.(D)

H

VI. 同義字整理：

1. **hate** 〔 het 〕 v. 恨
   - = dislike 〔 dɪs'laɪk 〕
   - = detest 〔 dɪ'tɛst 〕
   - = loathe 〔 loð 〕
   - = be hostile to

2. **hurt** 〔 hɜt 〕 v. 傷害
   - = harm 〔 hɑrm 〕
   - = injure 〔 'ɪndʒɚ 〕
   - = wound 〔 wund 〕
   - = damage 〔 'dæmɪdʒ 〕

3. **hesitate** 〔 'hɛzə,tet 〕 v. 猶豫
   - = wait 〔 wet 〕
   - = waver 〔 'wevɚ 〕
   - = falter 〔 'fɔltɚ 〕
   - = be uncertain

4. **howl** 〔 haʊl 〕 v. 怒吼
   - = roar 〔 ror 〕
   - = yell 〔 jɛl 〕
   - = shout 〔 ʃaʊt 〕
   - = scream 〔 skrim 〕

5. **harass** 〔 hə'ræs 〕 v. 騷擾
   - = annoy 〔 ə'nɔɪ 〕
   - = bother 〔 'bɑðɚ 〕

   - = disturb 〔 dɪ'stɜb 〕
   - = trouble 〔 'trʌbl̩ 〕

6. **humiliate** 〔 hju'mɪlɪ,et 〕 v. 使丟臉
   - = shame 〔 ʃem 〕
   - = disgrace 〔 dɪs'gres 〕
   - = degrade 〔 dɪ'gred 〕
   - = embarrass 〔 ɪm'bærəs 〕

7. **harsh** 〔 hɑrʃ 〕 adj. 嚴厲的
   - = hard 〔 hɑrd 〕
   - = tough 〔 tʌf 〕
   - = grim 〔 grɪm 〕
   - = severe 〔 sə'vɪr 〕

8. **hasty** 〔 'hestɪ 〕 adj. 匆忙的
   - = rash 〔 ræʃ 〕
   - = reckless 〔 'rɛklɪs 〕
   - = rushed 〔 rʌʃt 〕
   - = hurried 〔 'hɜɪd 〕

9. **hysterical** 〔 hɪs'tɛrɪkl̩ 〕 adj. 歇斯底里的
   - = frantic 〔 'fræntɪk 〕
   - = frenzied 〔 'frɛnzɪd 〕
   - = raving 〔 'revɪŋ 〕
   - = mad 〔 mæd 〕

H

Good Advice: What Not to Do

12. I (1)

看英文唸出中文	一 口 氣 説 九 句		看中文唸出英文
invade [4] 〔 ɪn'ved 〕 v.	字首都是 in	Don't *invade*. 不要干擾別人。	入侵；干擾
indulge [5] 〔 ɪn'dʌldʒ 〕 v.		*Indulge*. 不要沈迷於壞習慣。	使沈迷
intrude [6] 〔 ɪn'trud 〕 v.		*Intrude*. 不要打擾別人。	闖入；打擾

---

interfere [4] 〔 ͵ɪntɚ'fɪr 〕 v.	字首都是 Int	*Interfere*. 不要干涉別人的事。	干涉
interrupt [3] 〔 ͵ɪntə'rʌpt 〕 v.		*Interrupt*. 不要打斷別人。	打斷
intimidate [6] 〔 ɪn'tɪmə͵det 〕 v.		*Intimidate* others. 不要威脅別人。	威脅

---

insult [4] 〔 ɪn'sʌlt 〕 v.	字首是 In	*Insult* others. 不要侮辱別人。	都有 others	侮辱
injure [3] 〔 'ɪndʒɚ 〕 v.		*Injure* others. 不要傷害別人。		傷害
irritate [6] 〔 'ɪrə͵tet 〕 v.		*Irritate* others. 不要激怒別人。		激怒

I

I. 背景説明：

    Don't invade. 中的 invade，主要的意思是「入侵；侵犯」，在此作「干擾」解。這句話字面的意思是「不要入侵。」引申爲「不要干擾別人。」可說成：***Don't invade*** the privacy of others. (不要侵犯他人的隱私。) ***Don't invade*** the personal space of other people. (不要侵犯別人的個人空間。)

> 【比較】不要被中文思想誤導，invade 的後面不能接人。
>
>   Don't ***invade.***【正】
>
>   *Don't invade others.*【誤】
>
>   Don't ***invade*** others' privacy.【正】
>
> 中文說「干擾人」，英文不能用 *invade people*【誤】，因爲 invade 來自「入侵」。The army ***invaded*** our territory.（軍隊入侵我們的領土。)「干擾」是 invade 引申的意思。

Don't invade my room again.
(不要再闖入我的房間了。)

Sorry, my mistake.
(抱歉，是我的錯。)

Indulge. 在此指 Don't ***indulge.*** (不要沈迷。) 也就是 Don't ***indulge*** in bad habits. (不要沈迷於壞習慣。) Don't ***indulge*** in smoking or drinking. (不要沈迷於抽煙或喝酒。) *Intrude.* 在此指

Don't *intrude*.（不要打擾別人。）和 Don't *invade*. 意思相同。
可說成：Don't *intrude* on others.（不要打擾別人。）Don't
intrude on conversations.（不要插嘴。）

　　Interfere. 在此指 Don't *interfere*.（不要干涉。）Don't
interfere in personal matters.（不要干涉個人的事務。）Don't
interfere in business matters.（不要干涉公事。）*Interrupt*. 在
此指 Don't *interrupt*.（= *Don't interrupt people*.）Don't
interrupt people when they're working.（當人們工作時不要
打斷他們。）Don't *interrupt* others when they're speaking.
（當別人在講話時不要插嘴。）*Intimidate others*. 在此指
Don't *intimidate others*.
（不要威脅別人。）(= *Don't
intimidate people*.) Don't
try to *intimidate* people.
（不要想去威脅人。）Don't
intimidate or threaten
others.（不要威脅別人。）

　　Insult others. 在此指 Don't *insult others*.（不要侮辱別
人。）(= *Don't insult people*.) Don't be rude or *insult others*.
（不要粗魯或侮辱別人。）*Injure others*. 在此指 Don't *injure*
others.（不要傷害別人。）(= *Don't injure people*.) Avoid
injuring others.（要避免傷害別人。）*Irritate others*. 在此指
Don't *irritate others*.（不要激怒別人。）(= *Don't irritate*
people.) Don't *irritate* or annoy others.（不要激怒或使人心
煩。）

II. 英語演講：

【一字英語演講】 | 【短篇英語演講】

My dearest students:

My dearest students: 我最親愛的同學們：

Don't invade.
Indulge.
Intrude.

Don't invade the privacy of others.
不要侵犯別人的隱私。
Don't *indulge* in bad habits. 不要沈迷於壞習慣。
Don't *intrude* on others. 不要打擾別人。

Interfere.
Interrupt.
Intimidate others.

Don't *interfere* in business matters. 不要干涉公事。
Don't *interrupt* people when they're working.
當人們工作時不要打斷他們。
Don't *intimidate* or threaten *others*.
不要威脅別人。

Insult others.
Injure others.
Irritate others.

Don't be rude or *insult others*.
不要粗魯或侮辱別人。
Don't *injure others*. 不要傷害別人。
Don't *irritate* or annoy *others*.
不要激怒或使人心煩。

Take my advice and mind your own business.

Take my advice and mind your own business.
聽從我的勸告，管好自己的事。

III. 短篇作文：

Mind Your Own Business

The best advice is to mind your own business. *Therefore,* don't *invade* others' privacy. Don't *indulge* in smoking or drinking. *Besides*, don't *intrude* on others. *Likewise*, don't *interfere* in personal matters. Don't *interrupt* others when they're speaking. Don't try to *intimidate* people. *Moreover*, don't *insult* people. Avoid *injuring others*. *And finally*, don't *irritate* people with inappropriate questions, and mind your own business.

管好自己的事

　　最好的建議，就是管好自己的事。因此，不要侵犯別人的隱私。不要沈迷於抽煙或喝酒。此外，不要打擾別人。同樣地，不要干涉個人的事務。當別人在講話時不要插嘴。不要想去威脅別人。而且，不要侮辱別人。要避免傷害別人。最後，不要用不適當的問題激怒別人，並且管好自己的事。

> * *mind one's own business* 管好自己的事；少管閒事
> privacy〔'praɪvəsɪ〕*n.* 隱私（權）
> inappropriate〔ˌɪnə'proprɪɪt〕*adj.* 不適當的

IV. 填空：

　　First, don't ___1___ the privacy of others. Don't ___2___ in bad habits like smoking or drinking. Don't ___3___ on others.

　　Next, don't ___4___ in business matters. Don't ___5___ people when they're working. Don't ___6___ or threaten others.

　　Moreover, don't be rude or ___7___ others. Don't ___8___ or hurt people. Above all, mind your own business and don't ___9___ or annoy others.

　　首先，不要侵犯別人的隱私。不要沈迷於像是抽煙或喝酒的壞習慣。不要打擾別人。

　　其次，不要干涉公事。當人們工作時，不要打斷他們。不要威脅別人。

　　此外，不要粗魯或侮辱別人。不要傷害人。最重要的是，要管好自己的事，不要激怒或使人心煩。

【解答】 1. invade　2. indulge　3. intrude　4. interfere
　　　　　5. interrupt　6. intimidate　7. insult　8. injure
　　　　　9. irritate
　　　　　* threaten〔'θrɛtn̩〕*v.* 威脅　　rude〔rud〕*adj.* 粗魯的

V. 詞彙題 :

Directions: *Choose the one word that best completes the sentence.*

1. Be aware of your surroundings and don't _____ anybody's personal space.

   (A) involve   (B) invest   (C) invent   (D) invade

2. Resist the temptation to _____ in risky behavior.

   (A) intend   (B) inspire   (C) install   (D) indulge

3. Be careful not to _____ on conversations unless invited to speak.

   (A) insure   (B) intrude   (C) instruct   (D) inherit

4. It's best not to _____ in matters that don't concern you.

   (A) interact   (B) integrate   (C) interfere   (D) intensify

5. Think twice before _____ someone's conversation.

   (A) interrupting   (B) interpreting   (C) introducing
   (D) interviewing

6. Words meant to _____ someone could also be viewed as a threat.

   (A) include   (B) initiate   (C) intimidate   (D) inhabit

7. A good speaker doesn't _____ the intelligence of his audience.

   (A) infect   (B) insult   (C) improve   (D) imitate

8. If you're careless and _____ someone, you'll pay a heavy price.

   (A) injure   (B) illustrate   (C) imagine   (D) impress

9. Having a bad attitude will _____ everybody around you.

   (A) identify   (B) inform   (C) infer   (D) irritate

【答案】 1. (D)   2. (D)   3. (B)   4. (C)   5. (A)   6. (C)
　　　　7. (B)   8. (A)   9. (D)

VI. 同義字整理：

1. **invade** (ɪn'ved) v. 入侵；干擾
   = disturb (dɪ'stɝb)
   = interrupt (ˌɪntə'rʌpt)
   = violate ('vaɪəˌlet)
   = intrude on
   = trespass on

2. **indulge** (ɪn'dʌldʒ) v. 使沈迷
   = satisfy ('sætɪsˌfaɪ)
   = gratify ('grætəˌfaɪ)
   = yield to
   = give way to

3. **intrude** (ɪn'trud) v. 闖入；打擾
   = interrupt (ˌɪntə'rʌpt)
   = interfere with
   = invade (ɪn'ved)
   = trespass on

4. **interfere** (ˌɪntə'fɪr) v. 干涉
   = intrude (ɪn'trud)
   = meddle ('mɛdl̩)
   = intervene (ˌɪntə'vin)
   = get involved

5. **interrupt** (ˌɪntə'rʌpt) v. 打斷
   = disturb (dɪ'stɝb)
   = intrude (ɪn'trud)
   = interfere (ˌɪntə'fɪr)
   = intervene (ˌɪntə'vin)
   = cut off

6. **intimidate** (ɪn'tɪməˌdet) v. 威脅
   = threaten ('θrɛtn̩)
   = frighten ('fraɪtn̩)
   = scare (skɛr)
   = terrify ('tɛrəˌfaɪ)

7. **insult** (ɪn'sʌlt) v. 侮辱
   = offend (ə'fɛnd)
   = humiliate (hju'mɪlɪˌet)
   = put down

8. **injure** ('ɪndʒɚ) v. 傷害
   = hurt (hɝt)
   = wound (wund)
   = harm (harm)

9. **irritate** ('ɪrəˌtet) v. 激怒
   = annoy (ə'nɔɪ)
   = anger ('æŋgɚ)
   = bother ('baðɚ)
   = upset (ʌp'sɛt)

I

Good Advice: What Not to Do

13. I (2)

看英文唸出中文	一 口 氣 說 九 句	看中文唸出英文
ignore[2] 〔 ɪɡˋnor 〕 v.	三個動詞 { Don't *ignore* others. 不要忽視別人。	忽視
isolate[4] 〔ˋaɪslͺet〕 v.	*Isolate* yourself. 不要使自己和別人隔離。	使隔離
impose[5] 〔 ɪmˋpoz 〕 v.	*Impose*. 不要麻煩別人。	強加；麻煩
idle[4] 〔ˋaɪdl̩〕 adj.	三個形容詞 { Don't be *idle*. 不要遊手好閒。	懶惰的
ignorant[4] 〔ˋɪɡnərənt〕 adj.	*Ignorant*. 不要無知。	無知的
irritable[6] 〔ˋɪrətəbl̩〕 adj.	*Irritable*. 不要動不動就生氣。	易怒的
indifferent[5] 〔 ɪnˋdɪfrənt 〕 adj.	字首是 Indi { *Indifferent*. 不要漠不關心。	漠不關心的
indignant[5] 〔 ɪnˋdɪɡnənt 〕 adj.	*Indignant*. 不要憤憤不平。	憤怒的
idiot[5] 〔ˋɪdɪət〕 n.	An *idiot*. 不要當個白痴。	白痴

I. 背景説明：

　　Don't ignore others.（不要忽視別人。）(= *Don't ignore people.*) Don't ***ignore*** your responsibility.（不要忽視你的責任。）Don't ***ignore*** your loved ones.（不要忽視你心愛的人。）***Isolate yourself.*** 在此指 Don't ***isolate yourself.*** 可説成：Don't ***isolate yourself*** from others.（不要使自己和別人隔離。）Don't ***isolate*** your friends.（不要隔離你的朋友。）(= *Don't push your friends away.*) ***Impose.*** 在此指 Don't ***impose.*** 句中的 impose，主要的意思是「強加」，可引申爲：①利用②佔便宜③打擾④麻煩。Don't ***impose*** on people.（不要麻煩別人。）Don't ***impose*** your will on others.（不要把你的意志強加在別人身上。）

　　Don't be idle.（不要遊手好閒。）(= *Don't be an idle person.*) 可説成：Don't be ***idle*** or lazy.（不要懶惰。）***Ignorant.*** 在此指 Don't be ***ignorant.***（不要無知。）(= *Don't be an ignorant person.*) Don't be ***ignorant*** or uneducated.（不要無知。）***Irritable.*** 在此指 Don't be ***irritable.***（不要動不動就生氣。）(= *Don't be an irritable person.*) Don't be ***irritable*** under stress.（不要一有壓力就生氣。）Don't be ***irritable*** and harsh.（不要易怒又嚴厲。）

    Indifferent. 在此指 Don't be ***indifferent***. (不要漠不關心。) Don't be ***indifferent*** to others. (不要對別人漠不關心。) Don't be ***indifferent*** to your work. (不要對你的工作漠不關心。) *Indignant.* 在此指 Don't be ***indignant***. (不要憤憤不平。) (= *Don't be an indignant person.*) Don't be ***indignant*** or ungrateful. (不要憤憤不平或不知感謝。) Don't be ***indignant*** and demanding. (不要憤憤不平又苛求。) *An idiot.* 在此指 Don't be ***an idiot***. (不要當個白痴。) Don't be an ***idiot*** and a fool. (不要當個笨蛋。) Don't be an ***idiot*** about money. (不要亂用錢。) (= *Be wise with your money.*)

Friends:

Don't ignore others.
Isolate yourself.
Impose.

Don't be idle.
Ignorant.
Irritable.

Indifferent.
Indignant.
An idiot.

Take my advice and don't ignore these rules.

II. 短篇英語演講：

Friends: 朋友們：

Don't ignore others. 不要忽視別人。
Don't *isolate yourself* from others. 不要使自己和別人隔離。
Don't *impose* on people. 不要麻煩別人。

Don't be an *idle* person. 不要遊手好閒。
Don't be *ignorant* or uneducated. 不要無知。
Don't be *irritable* under stress. 不要一有壓力就生氣。

Don't be *indifferent* to others. 不要對別人漠不關心。
Don't be *indignant* and demanding.
不要憤憤不平又苛求。

Don't be *an idiot* and a fool. 不要當個笨蛋。

Take my advice and don't ignore these rules.
要聽從我的勸告，不要忽視這些原則。

III. 短篇作文：

Don't Ignore the Rules

There are certain rules in life. *First, don't ignore others.*
Don't *isolate yourself* by pushing your friends away. *Likewise,*
don't *impose* your will on others. *What's more, don't be idle*
or lazy. Don't be an *ignorant* person. Don't be *irritable* and
harsh. *Of course*, don't be *indifferent* to your work. Don't be
indignant or ungrateful. Don't be *an idiot* about money. *In*
the end, if you follow the rules, you'll have a happy life.

I

不要忽視這些原則

人生中有某些原則。首先,不要忽視別人。不要把朋友推開,使自己和別人隔離。同樣地,不要把你的意志強加在別人身上。此外,不要懶惰。不要做一個無知的人。不要易怒又嚴厲。當然,不要對你的工作漠不關心。不要憤憤不平或不知感謝。不要亂用錢。最後,如果你遵守這些原則,你就會有快樂的生活。

* certain (ˈsɝtn̩) *adj.* 某些　　will (wɪl) *n.* 意志
　ungrateful (ʌnˈgretfəl) *adj.* 不感激的

IV. 填空:

The number one rule is: don't ＿＿1＿＿ people who might need your help. Likewise, don't ＿＿2＿＿ yourself from others. Don't ＿＿3＿＿ your will on others.

Furthermore, don't be an ＿＿4＿＿ person. Don't be ＿＿5＿＿ or uneducated. Don't be ＿＿6＿＿ under stress.

Finally, don't be ＿＿7＿＿ to others. Don't be ＿＿8＿＿ and demanding. Don't be an ＿＿9＿＿ and a fool.

第一個原則就是:不要忽視可能需要你幫助的人。同樣地,不要使自己和別人隔離。不要把你的意志強加在別人身上。

此外,不要做一個遊手好閒的人。不要無知。不要一有壓力就生氣。

最後,不要對別人漠不關心。不要憤憤不平又苛求。不要當個笨蛋。

【解答】 1. ignore　2. isolate　3. impose　4. idle
　　　　5. ignorant　6. irritable　7. indifferent
　　　　8. indignant　9. idiot
　　　* stress (strɛs) *n.* 壓力
　　　　demanding (dɪˈmændɪŋ) *adj.* 苛求的

V. 詞彙題：

Directions: *Choose the one word that best completes the sentence.*

1. _____ your problems doesn't make them go away.
   (A) Imitating (B) Ignoring (C) Importing (D) Implying

2. By _____ yourself, you only make things worse.
   (A) issuing (B) ironing (C) investing (D) isolating

3. Good guests don't _____ on their hosts by staying too late.
   (A) immigrate (B) implement (C) impose (D) imagine

4. Some people are content to be _____ and let others do all the work.
   (A) idle (B) immune (C) ideal (D) identical

5. Never argue with an _____ person.
   (A) implicit (B) ignorant (C) incidental (D) inclusive

6. If you notice that someone is _____, leave him alone.
   (A) industrial (B) inherent (C) irritable (D) intimate

7. It's better to remain _____ to conflicts between others.
   (A) invaluable (B) internal (C) intellectual (D) indifferent

8. Think twice before you act _____.
   (A) infinitely (B) immensely (C) innumerably
   (D) indignantly

9. No one respects an _____.
   (A) idiot (B) idol (C) inventor (D) instructor

【答案】 1. (B) 2. (D) 3. (C) 4. (A) 5. (B) 6. (C)
       7. (D) 8. (D) 9. (A)

VI. 同義字整理：

1. **ignore** ﹝ ɪgˈnor ﹞ *v.* 忽視
   - = neglect ﹝ nɪˈglɛkt ﹞
   - = disregard ﹝ ˌdɪsrɪˈgɑrd ﹞
   - = overlook ﹝ ˌovɚˈluk ﹞
   - = pay no attention to

2. **isolate** ﹝ ˈaɪsḷˌet ﹞ *v.* 使隔離
   - = separate ﹝ ˈsɛpəˌret ﹞
   - = seclude ﹝ sɪˈklud ﹞
   - = segregate ﹝ ˈsɛgrɪˌget ﹞
   - = cut off

3. **impose** ﹝ ɪmˈpoz ﹞ *v.* 強加；麻煩
   - = exploit ﹝ ɪkˈsplɔɪt ﹞
   - = trouble ﹝ ˈtrʌbḷ ﹞
   - = intrude on
   - = take advantage of

4. **idle** ﹝ ˈaɪdḷ ﹞ *adj.* 懶惰的；遊手好閒的
   - = lazy ﹝ ˈlezɪ ﹞
   - = inactive ﹝ ɪnˈæktɪv ﹞
   - = stationary ﹝ ˈsteʃənˌɛrɪ ﹞
   - = out of work

5. **ignorant** ﹝ ˈɪgnərənt ﹞ *adj.* 無知的
   - = unaware ﹝ ˌʌnəˈwɛr ﹞
   - = insensitive ﹝ ɪnˈsɛnsətɪv ﹞
   - = unlearned ﹝ ʌnˈlɝnɪd ﹞
   - = uneducated ﹝ ʌnˈɛdʒuˌketɪd ﹞

6. **irritable** ﹝ ˈɪrətəbḷ ﹞ *adj.* 易怒的
   - = tense ﹝ tɛns ﹞
   - = touchy ﹝ ˈtʌtʃɪ ﹞
   - = bad-tempered ﹝ ˈbædˈtɛmpɚd ﹞

7. **indifferent** ﹝ ɪnˈdɪfrənt ﹞ *adj.* 漠不關心的
   - = cold ﹝ kold ﹞
   - = aloof ﹝ əˈluf ﹞
   - = careless ﹝ ˈkɛrlɪs ﹞
   - = detached ﹝ dɪˈtætʃt ﹞
   - = unconcerned ﹝ ˌʌnkənˈsɝnd ﹞

8. **indignant** ﹝ ɪnˈdɪgnənt ﹞ *adj.* 憤怒的
   - = angry ﹝ ˈæŋgrɪ ﹞
   - = annoyed ﹝ əˈnɔɪd ﹞
   - = furious ﹝ ˈfjurɪəs ﹞
   - = provoked ﹝ prəˈvokt ﹞

9. **idiot** ﹝ ˈɪdɪət ﹞ *n.* 白痴
   - = fool ﹝ ful ﹞
   - = moron ﹝ ˈmɔrən ﹞
   - = simpleton ﹝ ˈsɪmpḷtən ﹞

Good Advice: What Not to Do

14. J , L

看英文唸出中文	一口氣説九句	看中文唸出英文

judge²
〔 dʒʌdʒ 〕 v.

三個是 j 開頭

Don't judge.
不要批評。
判斷；批評

jeer⁵
〔 dʒɪr 〕 v.

Jeer.
不要嘲笑。
嘲笑

jaywalk⁵
〔'dʒe͵wɔk 〕 v.

Jaywalk.
不要擅自穿越馬路。
擅自穿越馬路

---

lie¹
〔 laɪ 〕 v.

字首是 Li

Lie.
不要說謊。
説謊

litter³
〔'lɪtɚ 〕 v.

Litter.
不要亂丟垃圾。
亂丟垃圾

lament⁶
〔 lə'mɛnt 〕 v.

Lament.
不要哀傷。
哀傷

---

lonely²
〔'lonlɪ 〕 adj.

字首都是 lo

Don't be lonely.
不要孤單。
孤單的

同義字

lonesome⁵
〔'lonsəm 〕 adj.

Lonesome.
不要寂寞。
寂寞的

loser²
〔'luzɚ 〕 n.

A loser.
不要當個輸家。
輸家

J

I. 背景說明：

> *Don't judge.* 中的 judge，可作「判斷」或「批評」解，在此作「批評」解。*Don't judge* others. (不要批評別人。) *Don't judge* a book by its cover. (【諺】人不可貌相。) 字面的意思是「不要只憑封面判斷一本書的好壞。」*Jeer.* 在此指 Don't *jeer*. (不要嘲笑。) Don't *jeer* at others. (不要嘲笑別人。) Don't *jeer* at or ridicule others. (不要去嘲笑別人。)【ridicule (ˈrɪdɪˌkjul) v. 嘲笑】*Jaywalk.* 在此指 Don't *jaywalk*. (不要擅自穿越馬路。) Don't *jaywalk* on busy streets. (在熱鬧的街上不要擅自穿越馬路。) jaywalk 是由 jay (快樂的) 和 walk (走路) 組成，「快樂地走」就是「擅自穿越馬路」。jaywalk 可能指闖紅燈，或沒走斑馬線 (pedestrian crosswalk)。

Lie. 在此指 Don't *lie*. (不要說謊。) 在美國，只要說一次謊，你說的所有的話，別人都不會再相信了。Don't *lie* to people. (不要對人說謊。) Don't *lie* or cheat. (不要說謊或欺騙。) *Litter.* 在此指 Don't *litter*. (不要亂丟垃圾。) litter 背不下來，可和 little (小的) 比較。Don't *litter* and pollute the environment. (不要亂丟垃圾，污染環境。) *Lament.* 在此指 Don't *lament*. (不要哀傷。) (= *Don't grieve.*) Don't *lament* your misfortune. (不要為你的不幸而哀傷。) Don't *lament* lost time. (不要為失去的時間哀傷。)

Don't be *lonely*. 有兩個意思，一是「不要單獨一個人。」(= *Don't be alone.*) 第二個是「不要寂寞。」(= *Don't be lonesome.*) 所以翻成「不要孤單。」包含兩個意思。Don't be *lonely* and shy. (不要孤單又害羞。) *Lonesome.* 在此指 Don't be *lonesome*. (不要寂寞。) Don't be *lonesome* and solitary. (不要寂寞又孤獨。) Find some friends to avoid feeling *lonesome*. (找一些朋友來避免寂寞。) *A loser.* 在此指 Don't be *a loser*. (不要當個輸家。) Don't be *a loser* or a jerk. (不要當個輸家或爛人。)【jerk (dʒɝk) n. 笨蛋；王八蛋】

II. 英語演講：

【一字英語演講】

Friends, I have
some advice:

Don't judge.
Jeer.
Jaywalk.

Lie.
Litter.
Lament.

Don't be lonely.
Lonesome.
A loser.

This is the best
advice.

【短篇英語演講】

Friends, I have some advice:
朋友們，我有一些建議：

Don't judge others.　不要批評別人。
Don't *jeer* at people.　不要嘲笑別人。
Don't *jaywalk* on busy streets.
在熱鬧的街上不要擅自穿越馬路。

Don't *lie* or cheat.　不要說謊或欺騙。
Don't be a person who *litters*.
不要做一個會亂丟垃圾的人。
Don't *lament* lost time.　不要爲失去的時間哀傷。

Don't be lonely and shy.　不要孤單又害羞。
Don't be *lonesome* and solitary.
不要寂寞又孤獨。
Don't be *a loser* or a jerk.　不要當個輸家或爛人。

This is the best advice.　這些是最好的建議。

III. 短篇作文：

The Best Advice

The best advice you may ever hear is: *Don't judge* a book by its cover. *Meanwhile*, don't *jeer* at or ridicule others. Don't *jaywalk*. *On top of that*, don't *lie* to people. Don't *litter* and pollute the environment. Don't *lament* your misfortune. *What's more*, *don't be* a *lonely* person. Find some friends to avoid feeling *lonesome*. *Finally*, don't be *a loser*. This is the best advice for success and happiness.

J

最好的建議

你可能會聽到的最好的建議就是：不要以貌取人。同時，不要嘲笑別人。不要擅自穿越馬路。此外，不要對人說謊。不要亂丟垃圾，污染環境。不要爲你的不幸而哀傷。而且，不要成爲孤單的人。要找一些朋友來避免寂寞。最後，不要當個輸家。這是要成功和快樂最好的建議。

> * cover〔ˋkʌvɚ〕*n.* 封面
> misfortune〔mɪsˋfɔrtʃən〕*n.* 不幸　　ever〔ˋɛvɚ〕*adv.* 曾經

IV. 填空：

First of all, don't ___1___ others before knowing them. Don't ___2___ at people; it's rude. Don't ___3___ on busy streets.

Second, don't ___4___, steal, or cheat. Don't be one of those people that ___5___ and pollute the environment. Don't ___6___ lost time.

Moreover, don't be a ___7___ and shy person. Don't be a ___8___ and solitary character. Above all, don't be a ___9___ or a jerk.

首先，在了解別人之前，不要批評他們。不要嘲笑別人；那很無禮。在熱鬧的街上不要擅自穿越馬路。

其次，不要說謊、偷竊，或欺騙。不要當一個會亂丟垃圾，污染環境的人。不要爲失去的時間哀傷。

此外，不要做一個孤單又害羞的人。不要做一個寂寞又孤獨的人。最重要的是，不要當個輸家或爛人。

【解答】 1. judge　2. jeer　3. jaywalk　4. lie　5. litter
　　　　 6. lament　7. lonely　8. lonesome　9. loser

> * busy〔ˋbɪzɪ〕*adj.* 熱鬧的　　shy〔ʃaɪ〕*adj.* 害羞的
> solitary〔ˋsɑlə,tɛrɪ〕*adj.* 孤獨的

V. 詞彙題：

Directions: *Choose the one word that best completes the sentence.*

1. Don't _____ a book by its cover.

　(A) judge　(B) jog　(C) join　(D) jump

2. It's very uncivilized to _____ at others.

　(A) justify　(B) jingle　(C) jar　(D) jeer

3. _____ isn't just dangerous; it's also against the law.

　(A) Journalism　(B) Jaywalking　(C) Jealousy　(D) Jungle

4. _____ leads to more trouble, so it's better to tell the truth.

　(A) Leaping　(B) Leaning　(C) Lying　(D) Laying

5. _____ is a crime against the environment and humanity.

　(A) Limiting　(B) Limping　(C) Littering　(D) Lingering

6. There's no time to _____ a loss.

　(A) launch　(B) lack　(C) lodge　(D) lament

7. Too many people live _____ lives.

　(A) lonely　(B) literary　(C) lunar　(D) lyric

8. There's nothing worse than living a _____ existence.

　(A) literate　(B) lonesome　(C) legal　(D) legislative

9. Be anything you want, but don't be a _____.

　(A) laser　(B) locker　(C) loser　(D) lobster

【答案】1.（A）　2.（D）　3.（B）　4.（C）　5.（C）　6.（D）
　　　　7.（A）　8.（B）　9.（C）

VI. 同義字整理：

1. judge〔dʒʌdʒ〕v. 判斷；批評

= view〔vju〕
= examine〔ɪg'zæmɪn〕
= evaluate〔ɪ'vælju,et〕
= criticize〔'krɪtə,saɪz〕

2. jeer〔dʒɪr〕v. 嘲笑

= mock〔mɑk〕
= sneer〔snɪr〕
= ridicule〔'rɪdɪ,kjul〕

3. jaywalk〔'dʒe,wɔk〕v. 擅自穿越馬路

= cross〔krɔs〕
= cut across
= cut through
= traverse〔'trævəs〕

4. lie〔laɪ〕v. 說謊

= invent〔ɪn'vɛnt〕
= fabricate〔'fæbrɪ,ket〕
= falsify〔'fɔlsə,faɪ〕

= tell a lie
= say something untrue

5. litter〔'lɪtə〕v. 亂丟垃圾

= scatter〔'skætə〕
= spread〔sprɛd〕
= mess up
= scatter about

6. lament〔lə'mɛnt〕v. 哀傷

= grieve〔griv〕
= mourn〔morn〕
= regret〔rɪ'grɛt〕
= weep over

7. lonely〔'lonlɪ〕adj. 孤單的

= solitary〔'sɑlə,tɛrɪ〕
= alone〔ə'lon〕
= lonesome〔'lonsəm〕
= isolated〔'aɪsḷ,etɪd〕

8. lonesome〔'lonsəm〕adj. 寂寞的

= lone〔lon〕
= lonely〔'lonlɪ〕
= isolated〔'aɪsḷ,etɪd〕
= friendless〔'frɛndlɪs〕

9. loser〔'luzə〕n. 輸家

= failure〔'feljə〕
= washout〔'wɑʃ,aut〕
= no-hoper〔'no'hopə〕
= non-achiever〔'nɑnə'tʃivə〕

J

Good Advice: What Not to Do

15. M

看英文唸出中文	一 口 氣 説 九 句	看中文唸出英文
murmur[4] 〔'mɜmə 〕 v.	三個是同義字、擬聲字	Don't *murmur*. 不要碎碎唸。	喃喃 自語
mutter[5] 〔'mʌtə 〕 v.		*Mutter*. 不要低聲說話。	喃喃地説
mumble[5] 〔'mʌmbḷ 〕 v.		*Mumble*. 不要含糊地說。	含糊地説

- -

mock[5] 〔 mɑk 〕 v.	由短到長	*Mock*. 不要嘲笑。	嘲弄
manipulate[6] 〔mə'nɪpjə‚let 〕 v.		*Manipulate*. 不要操縱。	操縱
mistake[1] 〔 mə'stek 〕 n.		Make a *mistake*. 不要犯錯。	錯誤

- -

miserable[4] 〔'mɪzərəbḷ 〕 adj.	三個是同義字	Don't be *miserable*. 不要悶悶不樂。	悲慘的
melancholy[6] 〔'mɛlən‚kɑlɪ 〕 adj.		*Melancholy*. 不要憂鬱。	憂鬱的
mournful[6] 〔'mɔrnfəl 〕 adj.		*Mournful*. 不要哀傷。	哀傷的

M

I. 背景説明:

> *Don't murmur.*（不要碎碎唸。）可説成：*Don't murmur*
> when you talk.（講話時不要太小聲。）(= *Don't speak in a low*
> *whisper.*) *Don't murmur* under your breath.（不要喃喃地低
> 聲説話。）【*under your breath* 壓低嗓子；低聲地】murmur 是擬
> 聲字，有兩個意思：①喃喃自語 (= *mumble*)；②低聲抱怨
> (= *complain*) 當一個人不停地小聲抱怨，就可以跟他説：
> *Don't murmur. Mutter.* 在此指 Don't *mutter.*（不要低聲説
> 話。）(= *Don't murmur.*) Don't *mutter* to yourself.（不要喃
> 喃自語。）Don't be a person that *mutters.*（不要做一個説話
> 含糊不清的人。）*Mumble.* 在此指 Don't *mumble.*（不要含糊
> 地説。）(= *Don't mumble your words.*) Don't *mumble* when
> you speak.（説話時不要含糊不清。）

> 【比較】聲音從小到大
> murmur → mutter → mumble
> （聽不見）　（聽不清楚）　（聽得見）

> *Mock.* 在此指 Don't *mock.*（不要嘲笑。）(= *Don't make*
> *fun.*) Don't *mock* people.（不要嘲笑人。）Don't *mock* or
> humiliate people.（不要嘲笑或羞辱人。）*Manipulate.* 在此指
> Don't *manipulate.*（不要操縱。）Don't *manipulate* others.
> （不要操縱別人。）Don't *manipulate* and mislead people.
> （不要操縱和誤導人。）*Make a mistake.* 在此指 Don't **make**
> **a mistake**. 可説成：Don't *make a* major *mistake.*（不要犯大
> 錯。）【major〔'medʒɚ〕*adj.* 主要的；重大的】Learn from your
> *mistakes.*（要從錯誤中學習。）

M

Don't be miserable. (不要悶悶不樂。) (= *Don't be depressed.*) Don't be a ***miserable*** person. (不要做一個不快樂的人。) 【 *miserable = unhappy* 】 Don't make others ***miserable.*** (不要讓別人不舒服。) 【 *miserable = very uncomfortable* 】 miserable 的意思有：「痛苦的；苦惱的；難受的；糟糕的；令人難受的；悲慘的；可悲的；身體不舒服的」，在此作「不快樂的」(= *unhappy*)、「沮喪的」(= *depressed*) 解。

What's wrong?
You look miserable.

I don't feel well.

Melancholy. 在此指 Don't be ***melancholy.*** (不要憂鬱。) (= *Don't be sad.*) Don't be ***melancholy*** or depressed. (不要憂鬱或沮喪。) Don't be a ***melancholy*** person. (不要做一個憂鬱的人。) *Mournful.* 在此指 Don't be ***mournful.*** (不要哀傷。) (= *Don't be sad.*) 可加強語氣說成：Don't be ***mournful*** and sad. (不要太悲傷。) Don't have a ***mournful*** expression. (不要有哀傷的表情。)

M

II. 英語演講：

【一字英語演講】　　【短篇英語演講】

Students, I have some good advice:

Students, I have some good advice:
同學們，我有一些很好的建議：

Don't murmur.
Mutter.
Mumble.

Don't murmur when you talk.
講話時不要太小聲。
Don't *mutter* to yourself.　不要喃喃自語。
Don't *mumble* your words.　不要含糊地說。

Mock.
Manipulate.
Make a mistake.

Don't *mock* people.　不要嘲笑人。
Don't *manipulate* others.　不要操縱別人。
Don't *make a* major *mistake*.　不要犯大錯。

Don't be miserable.
Melancholy.
Mournful.

Don't be a miserable person.
不要做一個不快樂的人。
Don't be *melancholy* or depressed.
不要憂鬱或沮喪。

This is really good advice.

Don't be *mournful* and sad.　不要太悲傷。

This is really good advice.　這些真的是很好的建議。

III. 短篇作文：

Really Good Advice

　　A wise man once gave me some good advice.　He said, *don't murmur* under your breath.　Don't *mutter* to yourself.　And don't *mumble* when you speak.　*Meanwhile*, don't *mock* or humiliate people.　Don't *manipulate* and mislead people.　Learn from your *mistakes* and move on.　*Likewise, don't be miserable*.　Nobody likes a *melancholy* character.　*And above all*, don't walk around with a *mournful* expression.　*Indeed*, that was some really good advice.

非常好的建議

有一位聰明的人曾經給我一些很好的建議。他說，不要喃喃地低聲說話。不要喃喃自語。而且說話時不要含糊地說。同時，不要嘲笑或羞辱人。不要操縱和誤導人。要從錯誤中學習，並繼續前進。同樣地，不要悶悶不樂。沒有人喜歡憂鬱的人。而且最重要的是，四處走動時，不要有哀傷的表情。的確，那是一些真的很好的建議。

* mislead (mɪs'lid) v. 誤導
  expression (ɪk'sprɛʃən) n. 表情

IV. 填空：

It's hard to understand people who ___1___ when they talk. Therefore, don't ___2___ to yourself. And don't ___3___ your words.

Additionally, don't ___4___ or humiliate people. Don't ___5___ others to get your way. Don't act foolishly and make a major ___6___.

On top of that, don't be a ___7___ person. Don't be a ___8___ or depressed character. Finally, don't be ___9___ and sad.

很難聽懂講話很小聲的人在說什麼。因此，不要喃喃自語。而且不要含糊地說。

此外，不要嘲笑或羞辱人。不要操縱別人，為所欲為。行為舉止不要愚蠢，犯下大錯。

除了那樣之外，不要做一個不快樂的人。不要做一個憂鬱或沮喪的人。最後，不要太悲傷。

【解答】 1. murmur　2. mutter　3. mumble　4. mock
　　　　 5. manipulate　6. mistake　7. miserable
　　　　 8. melancholy　9. mournful

M

V. 詞彙題：

Directions: *Choose the one word that best completes the sentence.*

1. Why _____ when you can speak clearly?
   (A) murmur　(B) murder　(C) mount　(D) motivate

2. _____ about a problem isn't going to solve anything.
   (A) Muttering　(B) Modernizing　(C) Mobilizing
   (D) Manufacturing

3. He _____ something about not wanting to go to work.
   (A) marveled　(B) managed　(C) mumbled　(D) marched

4. You will be _____ for having a poor understanding of
   current events.
   (A) mashed　(B) melted　(C) mediated　(D) mocked

5. Only the weakest people can be _____.
   (A) maintained　(B) manipulated　(C) memorized
   (D) meditated

6. Don't worry about who made the _____; just fix it.
   (A) message　(B) mistake　(C) massage　(D) mineral

7. There are countless ways to avoid being _____.
   (A) mental　(B) medieval　(C) middle　(D) miserable

8. Put on some upbeat music to cure a _____ mood.
   (A) memorable　(B) mighty　(C) melancholy　(D) miniature

9. Try mediating to shake a _____ feeling.
   (A) mournful　(B) mobile　(C) moral　(D) mutual

【答案】 1.(A)　2.(A)　3.(C)　4.(D)　5.(B)　6.(B)
　　　　 7.(D)　8.(C)　9.(A)

M

VI. 同義字整理：

1. **murmur** (ˈmɝmə) *v.* 喃喃自語

= mumble (ˈmʌmbḷ)
= whisper (ˈhwɪspə)
= mutter (ˈmʌtə)

2. **mutter** (ˈmʌtə) *v.* 喃喃地說

= murmur (ˈmɝmə)
= mumble (ˈmʌmbḷ)
= grumble (ˈgrʌmbḷ)

3. **mumble** (ˈmʌmbḷ) *v.* 含糊地說

= murmur (ˈmɝmə)
= mutter (ˈmʌtə)
= whisper (ˈhwɪspə)
= speak indistinctly

4. **mock** (mɑk) *v.* 嘲弄

= tease (tis)
= taunt (tɔnt)
= ridicule (ˈrɪdɪ,kjul)

= laugh at
= make fun of

5. **manipulate** (məˈnɪpjə,let) *v.* 操縱

= control (kənˈtrol)
= exploit (ɪkˈsplɔɪt)
= direct (dəˈrɛkt)
= influence (ˈɪnfluəns)

6. **mistake** (məˈstek) *n.* 錯誤

= error (ˈɛrə)
= blunder (ˈblʌndə)
= slip (slɪp)
= false move

7. **miserable** (ˈmɪzərəbḷ) *adj.*
悲慘的；不快樂的

= gloomy (ˈglumɪ)
= depressed (dɪˈprɛst)
= melancholy (ˈmɛlən,kɑlɪ)

8. **melancholy** (ˈmɛlən,kɑlɪ) *adj.*
憂鬱的

= down (daʊn)
= gloomy (ˈglumɪ)
= depressed (dɪˈprɛst)
= miserable (ˈmɪzərəbḷ)

9. **mournful** (ˈmɔrnfəl) *adj.*
哀傷的

= miserable (ˈmɪzərəbḷ)
= gloomy (ˈglumɪ)
= grieving (ˈgrivɪŋ)

= melancholy (ˈmɛlən,kɑlɪ)
= brokenhearted
(ˈbrokənˈhɑrtɪd)
= heartbroken (ˈhɑrt,brokən)

N

 Good Advice: What Not to Do

16. N

看英文唸出中文	一口氣説九句	看中文唸出英文
naughty[2] (ˈnɔtɪ) *adj.*	字首都是na {	**Don't be *naughty*.** 不要頑皮。	頑皮的
nasty[5] (ˈnæstɪ) *adj.*		***Nasty.*** 不要讓人討厭。	討厭的
narrow-minded (ˈnæro ˈmaɪndɪd) *adj.*		***Narrow-minded.*** 不要心胸狹窄。	心胸狹窄的

	字首都是Ne {		
needy[4] (ˈnidɪ) *adj.*		***Needy.*** 不要窮困。	窮困的
nervous[3] (ˈnɝvəs) *adj.*		***Nervous.*** 不要緊張。	緊張的
nearsighted[4] (ˈnɪrˈsaɪtɪd) *adj.*		***Nearsighted.*** 不要短視近利。	近視的

	字首是No {		
noisy[1] (ˈnɔɪzɪ) *adj.*		***Noisy.*** 不要吵鬧。	吵鬧的
notorious[6] (noˈtorɪəs) *adj.*		***Notorious.*** 不要惡名昭彰。	惡名昭彰的
nuisance[6] (ˈnjusn̩s) *n.*		**A *nuisance*.** 不要當個討厭的人。	討厭的人或物

N

I. 背景說明：

Don't be *naughty*. (不要頑皮。) (= *Don't be a naughty person.*) ***Don't be naughty*** and mischievous. (不要太頑皮。)【mischievous (ˈmɪstʃɪvəs) *adj.* 愛惡作劇的；頑皮的】*Nasty.* 在此指 Don't be *nasty*. (不要討人厭。) (= *Don't be unpleasant.*) Don't be a *nasty* person. (不要讓人討厭。) Don't be *nasty* to others. (不要對他人不懷好意。) (= *Don't be mean to others.*) Don't be *nasty* and mean. (不要太卑鄙。) nasty 的主要意思是「令人作嘔的」，引申為「令人厭惡的；討厭的；下流的；卑鄙的；邪惡的」。*Narrow-minded.* 在此指 Don't be *narrow-minded*. (不要心胸狹窄。) 可加強語氣說成：Don't be *narrow-minded* and conservative. (不要心胸狹窄又保守。) Don't be too *narrow-minded* to accept new information. (不要心胸太狹窄，而不能接受新資訊。)

Needy. 在此指 Don't be *needy*. (不要窮困。) (= *Don't be poor.*) Don't be *needy* and dependent on others. (不要窮困潦倒，依賴別人。) Don't be *needy* and weak. (不要窮困又虛弱。) *Nervous.* 在此指 Don't be *nervous*. (不要緊張。) 可加強語氣說成：Don't be *nervous* or anxious around other people. (有別人在不要緊張或焦慮。) Don't be a *nervous* character. (不要做一個緊張的人。) *Nearsighted.* 在此指 Don't be *nearsighted*. (不要短視近利。) nearsighted

N

的主要意思是「近視的」，在此作「短視近利的」解。Don't be *nearsighted* and shallow.（不要短視近利又膚淺。）

Noisy. 在此指 Don't be *noisy*.（不要吵鬧。）（= *Don't be a noisy person.*）*Noisy* people are annoying.（吵鬧的人很煩人。）*Notorious*. 在此指 Don't be *notorious*.（不要惡名昭彰。）（= *Don't be a notorious person.*）Don't associate with *notorious* people.（不要和名聲壞的人來往。）Avoid *notorious* places.（名聲不好的地方不要去。）*A nuisance*. 在此指 Don't be *a nuisance*.（不要當個討厭的人。）Don't be *a nuisance* to others.（不要讓人討厭。）Don't create *a nuisance*.（不要製造麻煩。）（= *Don't make trouble.*）nuisance 的意思有：①討厭的人或物②麻煩的事。

Ladies and gentlemen,
　allow me to offer some advice:

Don't be naughty.
Nasty.
Narrow-minded.

Needy.
Nervous.
Nearsighted.

Noisy.
Notorious.
A nuisance.

Thank you for accepting my offer.

II. 短篇英語演講：

Ladies and gentlemen, allow me to offer some advice:
各位先生，各位女士，讓我來提供一些建議：

Don't be a *naughty* person.　不要頑皮。
Don't be *nasty* to others.　不要對他人不懷好意。
Don't be *narrow-minded*.　不要心胸狹窄。

Don't be *needy* and weak.　不要窮困又虛弱。
Don't be a *nervous* character.　不要做一個緊張的人。
Don't be a *nearsighted* person.　不要短視近利。

Don't be a *noisy* person.　不要吵鬧。
Don't associate with *notorious* people.
不要和名聲壞的人來往。
Don't be *a nuisance* to others.　不要讓人討厭。

Thank you for accepting my offer.
謝謝你們接受我提供的建議。

III. 短篇作文：

An Offer of Advice

When someone offers you advice, you should take it.
Therefore, don't be naughty and mischievous.　Don't be *nasty*
and mean.　Don't be *narrow-minded* and conservative.
Additionally, don't be *needy* and dependent on others.　Don't be
nervous or anxious around other people.　Don't be *nearsighted*
and shallow.　*Most importantly, noisy* people are annoying.
Avoid *notorious* places.　Take this good advice and don't
create *a nuisance*.

N

提供建議

當有人提供建議給你，你就應該接受。因此，不要太頑皮。不要太卑鄙。不要心胸狹窄又保守。此外，不要窮困潦倒，依賴他人。有別人在不要緊張或焦慮，不要短視近利又膚淺。最重要的是，吵鬧的人很煩人。名聲不好的地方不要去。要接受這些好的建議，不要製造麻煩。

* mean〔 min 〕*adj.* 卑鄙的
  conservative〔 kən'sɝvətɪv 〕*adj.* 保守的
  anxious〔'æŋkʃəs 〕*adj.* 焦慮的　　shallow〔'ʃælo 〕*adj.* 膚淺的

IV. 填空：

To start with, don't be a ___1___ person. Don't be mean and ___2___ to others. Don't be too ___3___ to accept new information.

Moreover, don't have a ___4___ and weak personality. Don't be an anxious and ___5___ character. Don't be a ___6___ person.

Meanwhile, don't be a ___7___ and disruptive person. Don't associate with ___8___ people. Don't be a ___9___ to others.

首先，不要頑皮。對別人不要太卑鄙。不要心胸太狹窄，而不能接受新資訊。

此外，不要有窮困又虛弱的個性。不要做一個焦慮又緊張的人。不要做一個短視近利的人。

同時，不要做一個吵鬧又有破壞性的人。不要和名聲壞的人來往。不要讓人討厭。

【解答】 1. naughty　2. nasty　3. narrow-minded
　　　　 4. needy　5. nervous　6. nearsighted
　　　　 7. noisy　8. notorious　9. nuisance

* disruptive〔 dɪs'rʌptɪv 〕*adj.* 破壞性的；引起混亂的
  associate〔 ə'soʃɪˌet 〕*v.* 交往

V. 詞彙題：

Directions: Choose the one word that best completes the sentence.

1. Don't be _____ when you could be nice.
   (A) natural (B) naive (C) naughty (D) nude

2. _____ people are shunned by society.
   (A) Neutral (B) Nasty (C) Normal (D) Neat

3. Being _____ isn't going to help you in life.
   (A) naval (B) nutritious (C) numerous
   (D) narrow-minded

4. _____ people will find themselves with fewer and fewer
   friends.
   (A) Needy (B) Necessary (C) Nuclear (D) Noble

5. If public speaking makes you _____, practice your speech.
   (A) narrative (B) nervous (C) negative (D) nonviolent

6. You won't make any progress with a _____ view of the future.
   (A) naked (B) noted (C) nominated (D) nearsighted

7. If you're always _____, expect people to complain.
   (A) native (B) noisy (C) national (D) northern

8. Stay away from places that are _____ for crime.
   (A) notorious (B) nibbled (C) navigated (D) narrow

9. You're not going to be very popular if you're always creating
   a _____ .
   (A) nationality (B) notion (C) nuisance (D) network

【答案】 1.(C) 2.(B) 3.(D) 4.(A) 5.(B) 6.(D)
         7.(B) 8.(A) 9.(C)

VI. 同義字整理：

N

1. **naughty** (ˈnɔtɪ) *adj.* 頑皮的
   = mischievous (ˈmɪstʃɪvəs)
   = disobedient (ˌdɪsəˈbidɪənt)
   = bad (bæd)

2. **nasty** (ˈnæstɪ) *adj.* 討厭的；卑鄙
   的；邪惡的
   = mean (min)
   = vicious (ˈvɪʃəs)
   = unpleasant (ʌnˈplɛznt)
   = annoying (əˈnɔɪɪŋ)
   = foul (faʊl)
   = disgusting (dɪsˈgʌstɪŋ)

3. **narrow-minded** (ˈnæro ˈmaɪndɪd)
   adj. 心胸狹窄的
   = intolerant (ɪnˈtɑlərənt)
   = conservative (kənˈsɝvətɪv)
   = prejudiced (ˈprɛdʒədɪst)
   = shortsighted (ˈʃɔrtˈsaɪtɪd)

4. **needy** (ˈnidɪ) *adj.* 窮困的
   = poor (pʊr)
   = deprived (dɪˈpraɪvd)
   = disadvantaged
     (ˌdɪsədˈvæntɪdʒd)
   = impoverished (ɪmˈpɑvərɪʃt)

5. **nervous** (ˈnɝvəs) *adj.* 緊張的
   = tense (tɛns)
   = uneasy (ʌnˈizɪ)
   = anxious (ˈæŋkʃəs)
   = worried (ˈwɝɪd)
   = apprehensive (ˌæprɪˈhɛnsɪv)

6. **nearsighted** (ˈnɪrˈsaɪtɪd) *adj.*
   近視的；短視近利的
   = shortsighted (ˈʃɔrtˈsaɪtɪd)
   = lacking foresight

7. **noisy** (ˈnɔɪzɪ) *adj.* 吵鬧的
   = loud (laʊd)
   = rowdy (ˈraʊdɪ)
   = clamorous (ˈklæmərəs)

8. **notorious** (noˈtorɪəs) *adj.*
   惡名昭彰的
   = infamous (ˈɪnfəməs)
   = disreputable (dɪsˈrɛpjətəbl)
   = both widely and
     unfavorably known

9. **nuisance** (ˈnjusns) *n.* 討厭的
   人或物
   = pest (pɛst)
   = annoyance (əˈnɔɪəns)
   = pain in the ass

Good Advice: What Not to Do

17. O

看英文唸出中文	一口氣說九句	看中文唸出英文

O

overdo⁵
('ovɚ'du) v.

overeat⁵
('ovɚ'it) v.

oversleep⁵
('ovɚ'slip) v.

字首都是 over

Don't *overdo.*
不要做得過份。

Overeat.
不要吃太多。

Oversleep.
不要睡過頭。

做得過度

吃得過多

睡過頭

---

overwork⁵
('ovɚ'wɝk) v. n.

object²
(əb'dʒɛkt) v.

offend⁴
(ə'fɛnd) v.

Overwork.
不要工作過度。

Object.
不要反對。

Offend.
不要冒犯別人。

工作過度

反對

冒犯

---

obscure⁶
(əb'skjʊr) adj.

obstinate⁵
('abstənɪt) adj.

obstacle⁴
('abstəkḷ) n.

字首都是 obs

Don't be *obscure.*
不要讓人難以了解。

Obstinate.
不要頑固。

An *obstacle.*
不要成為阻礙。

模糊的

頑固的

阻礙

O

I. 背景説明：

Don't overdo. 可説成：Don't *overdo* it.（不要做得過份。）Don't *overdo* things.（事情不要做得過份。）*Overeat.* 在此指 Don't *overeat.*（不要吃太多。）If you *overeat*, you'll get fat.（如果你吃太多，就會變胖。）Don't *overeat* junk food.（不要吃太多垃圾食物。）*Oversleep.* 在此指 Don't *oversleep.*（不要睡過頭。）Don't *oversleep* and be late.（不要睡過頭遲到。）Don't *oversleep* and miss the bus.（不要睡過頭，錯過巴士。）

Overwork. 在此指 Don't *overwork.*（不要工作過度。）Don't *overwork* yourself.（自己不要工作過度。）（= *Don't overwork.*）Don't *overwork* your employees.（不要讓你的員工工作過度。）overwork 和 overtime（加班）不同。Don't work too much overtime.（不要加班太多。）*Object.* 在此指 Don't *object.*（不要反對。）遇到不合你意的事情，不要馬上反對。Don't *object* to suggestions.（不要反對建議。）Don't *object* to advice.（不要反對勸告。）Don't *object* to working.（不要反對工作。）【to 是介系詞，object to 後面接名詞或動名詞】*Offend.* 在此指 Don't *offend.*（不要冒犯別人。）（= *Don't offend others.*）Don't use words that may *offend* others.（不要說可能會冒犯別人的話。）Don't be easily *offended.*（不要很容易被激怒。）offend 的主要意思是「冒犯」，可引申爲「觸怒；激怒」。

Don't be obscure. (= *Don't be hard to understand.*) obscure
的主要意思是「模糊的」，在此作「難以了解的」解。可加強語氣
說成：Don't be *obscure* and hard to understand. （不要讓人捉摸
不定，難以了解。）Don't be an *obscure* character. （不要做一個
讓人捉摸不定的人。）*Obstinate.* 在此指 Don't be *obstinate*. （不
要頑固。）(= *Don't be an obstinate person.*) 可加強語氣說成：
Don't be *obstinate* and stubborn. （不要太固執。）obstinate 的
意思有：「頑固的；固執的；倔強的」。*Obstinate* people are
unpleasant. （頑固的人誰都不喜歡。）*An obstacle.* 在此指 Don't
be *an obstacle*. （不要成為阻礙。）(= *Don't be a problem.* = *Don't*
be in the way.) Don't worry about *obstacles*. （不要擔心阻礙。）
obstacle 的意思有：「障礙；阻礙；妨礙」。Conquer every *obstacle*.
（要征服每一個障礙。）

Students, I have some
excellent advice:

Don't overdo.
Overeat.
Oversleep.

Overwork.
Object.
Offend.

Don't be obscure.
Obstinate.
An obstacle.

This is excellent advice.

O

II. 短篇英語演講：

Students, I have some excellent advice:
同學們，我有一些很棒的建議：

Don't overdo things. 事情不要做得過份。

Don't **overeat** junk food. 不要吃太多垃圾食物。

Don't **oversleep** and be late. 不要睡過頭遲到。

Don't **overwork** yourself. 自己不要工作過度。

Don't **object** to suggestions. 不要反對建議。

Don't **offend** others. 不要冒犯別人。

Don't be an **obscure** character.
不要做一個讓人捉摸不定的人。

Don't be an **obstinate** person. 不要頑固。

Don't be **an obstacle** to yourself. 不要成爲你自己的阻礙。

This is excellent advice. 這些是很棒的建議。

III. 短篇作文：

Excellent Advice

Here is some excellent advice. *First of all*, **don't overdo** things. If you **overeat**, you'll get fat. Don't **oversleep** and be late. *Meanwhile*, don't **overwork** your employees. *Likewise*, don't **object** to suggestions. Don't use words that may **offend** others. **Don't be obscure** and hard to understand. *Indeed*, **obstinate** people are unpleasant. *Finally*, take this excellent advice and don't be **an obstacle**.

很棒的建議

以下是一些很棒的建議。首先,事情不要做得過份。如果你吃太多,就會變胖。不要睡過頭遲到。同時,不要讓你的員工工作過度。同樣地,不要反對建議。不要說可能會冒犯別人的話。不要讓人捉摸不定,難以了解。的確,頑固的人誰都不喜歡。最後,要聽從這些很棒的建議,不要成為阻礙。

* employee〔͵ɛmplɔɪˈi〕*n.* 員工
  unpleasant〔ʌnˈplɛznt〕*adj.* 令人不愉快的;令人討厭的

IV. 填空:

People who ___1___ things have a hard time in life. Therefore, don't ___2___ junk food. Don't forget to set your alarm, ___3___, and be late.

Furthermore, don't ___4___ yourself. Don't ___5___ to good advice when it's being offered. Don't be easily ___6___.

Most importantly, don't be an ___7___ character who talks about weird things. Don't be an ___8___ and stubborn person. Don't be an ___9___ to yourself.

事情做得過份的人,會過著辛苦的生活。因此,不要吃太多垃圾食物。不要忘了設鬧鐘,睡過頭,然後遲到。

此外,自己不要工作過度。當別人給你好的勸告時,不要反對。不要很容易被激怒。

最重要的是,不要做一個讓人捉摸不定的人,談論奇怪的事。不要太固執。不要成為你自己的阻礙。

【解答】 1. overdo   2. overeat   3. oversleep   4. overwork
5. object   6. offended   7. obscure   8. obstinate
9. obstacle

* alarm〔əˈlɑrm〕*n.* 鬧鐘 (= *alarm clock*)
  weird〔wɪrd〕*adj.* 奇怪的   stubborn〔ˈstʌbən〕*adj.* 頑固的

V. 詞彙題：

Directions: *Choose the one word that best completes the sentence.*

1. It's easy to _____ things if you're not a disciplined person.
   (A) obey   (B) oblige   (C) overdo   (D) observe

2. _____ is one of the worst things you can do to your body.
   (A) Overflowing   (B) Overturning   (C) Overeating
   (D) Overcoming

3. If you find yourself _____, try going to bed earlier.
   (A) offering   (B) oversleeping   (C) operating
   (D) oppressing

4. Many people _____ themselves and wind up having a heart attack.
   (A) order   (B) organize   (C) originate   (D) overwork

5. Have a good reason before _____ to a suggestion.
   (A) objecting   (B) obtaining   (C) observing   (D) occurring

6. Be careful what you say or you might _____ somebody.
   (A) overhear   (B) omit   (C) offend   (D) obey

7. The more _____ a person is, the harder he is to know.
   (A) obscure   (B) organic   (C) outdoor   (D) optional

8. Generally speaking, it's better to be flexible than _____.
   (A) obstinate   (B) outward   (C) occasional   (D) optimistic

9. Too many people put _____ in their own paths.
   (A) orchestras   (B) obstacles   (C) overpasses   (D) orbits

【答案】1.(C)　2.(C)　3.(B)　4.(D)　5.(A)　6.(C)
　　　　7.(A)　8.(A)　9.(B)

＊第6題 Be careful what you say…. = Be careful of what you say….

VI. 同義字整理：

1. overdo ('ovə'du) v. 做得過度

- = overwork ('ovə'wɜk)
- = overindulge ('ovəɪn'dʌldʒ)
- = go too far
- = go overboard

2. overeat ('ovə'it) v. 吃得過多

- = gorge (gɔrdʒ)
- = binge (bɪndʒ)
- = overindulge (,ovəɪn'dʌldʒ)

- = pig out
- = stuff *oneself*
- = drink or eat too much

3. oversleep ('ovə'slip) v. 睡過頭

- = sleep in
- = sleep longer than intended

4. overwork ('ovə'wɜk) v. n. 工作過度

- = wear yourself out
- = burn the candle at both ends
- = bite off more than you can chew
- = work your fingers to the bone

5. object (əb'dʒɛkt) v. 反對

- = disagree (,dɪsə'gri)
- = oppose (ə'poz)

- = argue against
- = say no to
- = express disapproval

6. offend (ə'fɛnd) v. 冒犯

- = upset (ʌp'sɛt)
- = outrage ('aut,redʒ)
- = provoke (prə'vok)
- = revolt (rɪ'volt)

7. obscure (əb'skjur) adj. 模糊的

- = vague (veg)
- = unclear (ʌn'klɪr)
- = confusing (kən'fjuzɪŋ)

8. obstinate ('abstənɪt) adj. 頑固的

- = stubborn ('stʌbən)
- = intractable (ɪn'træktəbl̩)
- = unyielding (ʌn'jildɪŋ)
- = pig-headed (,pɪg'hɛdɪd)

9. obstacle ('abstəkl̩) n. 阻礙

- = obstruction (əb'strʌkʃən)
- = impediment (ɪm'pɛdəmənt)
- = handicap ('hændɪ,kæp)
- = hindrance ('hɪndrəns)

Good Advice: What Not to Do

18. P

看英文唸出中文	一口氣說九句	看中文唸出英文

poke 5
〔 pok 〕 *v.*

poach 6
〔 potʃ 〕 *v.*

postpone 3
〔 post'pon 〕 *v.*

字首是 po

Don't poke.
不要干涉別人。

Poach.
不要竊取。

Postpone.
不要延期。

刺；戳；干涉

竊取

延期

---

preach 5
〔 pritʃ 〕 *v.*

pretend 3
〔 prɪ'tɛnd 〕 *v.*

provoke 6
〔 prə'vok 〕 *v.*

字首是 Pr

Preach.
不要說教。

Pretend.
不要作假。

Provoke.
不要激怒別人。

說教

假裝

激怒

---

punch 3
〔 pʌntʃ 〕 *v.*

puzzle 2
〔 'pʌzl̩ 〕 *v.*

pirate 4
〔 'paɪrət 〕 *v.*

字首是 Pu

Punch.
不要用拳頭打人。

Puzzle.
不要使人困惑。

Pirate.
不要盜版。

用拳頭打

使困惑

盜版

I. 背景説明：

　　你一定沒有聽過 *Don't poke*. 但美國人常說。它的字面意思是「不要戳。」(= *Don't jab.* = *Don't stab.*) Don't *poke* me in the back. (不要戳我的背。) 在這裡是指「不要干涉。」(= *Don't meddle.*) 或「不要打擾。」(= *Don't intrude.*) 完整的説法是：Don't *poke* into others' business. (不要干涉別人的事。) Don't *poke* people. (不要干涉別人。) Don't *poke* and provoke others. (不要干涉並激怒他人。) *Poach.* 在此指 Don't *poach*. (不要竊取。) poach 的主要意思是「偷獵」，在此引申為：①盜用 (= *take illegally*) ②竊取 (他人想法) (= *steal an idea*) ③挖角 (= *steal*)。Don't *poach* from others. (不要竊取別人的東西。) Don't *poach* what isn't yours. (不要竊取不是你的東西。) *Postpone.* 在此指 Don't *postpone*. (不要延期。) Don't *postpone* or delay. (不要延期或拖延。) Don't *postpone* important meetings. (重要的會議不要延期。)

　　Preach. 在此指 Don't *preach*. (不要說教。) (= *Don't lecture.*) Don't be a person who *preaches*. (不要做一個喜歡講道理的人。) Don't *preach* what you believe. (不要反覆灌輸你相信的事。) preach 的意思有：①佈道；講道 ②說教；訓誡 ③灌輸；竭力勸導。*Pretend.* 在此指 Don't *pretend*. (不要作假。) (= *Don't act falsely.*) Don't *pretend* to be honest. (不要假裝誠實。) Don't *pretend* to have

information when you don't. (當你沒有資訊時，不要假裝你有。)
Provoke. 在此指 Don't *provoke*. (不要激怒別人。) (= *Don't annoy others*.) Don't *provoke* others. (不要激怒別人。) Don't *provoke* or start fights with people. (不要激怒或挑釁別人。)

　　Punch. 在此指 Don't *punch*. 也就是 Don't *punch* people. (不要用拳頭打人。) Don't *punch* or hit others. (不要用拳頭打人。) *Puzzle.* 在此指 Don't *puzzle*. (不要使人困惑。) (= *Don't puzzle people*.) Don't be a *puzzling* person. (不要做一個令人費解的人。) *Pirate.* 在此指 Don't *pirate*. (不要盜版。) pirate 的主要意思是「海盜」，在此作「盜版」解。Don't *pirate* content from the Internet. (不要盜用網路上的內容。)

Students of all ages:

Don't poke.
Poach.
Postpone.

Preach.
Pretend.
Provoke.

Punch.
Puzzle.
Pirate.

Thank you for listening.

II. 短篇英語演講：

Students of all ages: 各位同學：

Don't poke into others' business. 不要干涉別人的事。
Don't *poach* from others. 不要竊取別人的東西。
Don't *postpone* important meetings. 重要的會議不要延期。

Don't be a person who *preaches*.
不要做一個喜歡講道理的人。
Don't *pretend* to be honest. 不要假裝誠實。
Don't *provoke* others. 不要激怒別人。

Don't *punch* or hit others. 不要用拳頭打人。
Don't be a *puzzling* person. 不要做一個令人費解的人。
Don't *pirate* content from the Internet.
不要盜用網路上的內容。

Thank you for listening. 謝謝大家的聆聽。

III. 短篇作文：

Advice from the Letter "P"

There is a lot of good advice from the letter "p". *To begin with*, *don't poke* and disturb others. Don't *poach* what isn't yours. *Additionally*, don't *postpone* or delay. Don't *preach* what you believe. Don't *pretend* to have information when you don't. *On top of that*, don't *provoke* or start fights with people. Don't *punch* people. Don't *puzzle* people. *And finally*, don't *pirate* material that you didn't pay for. Trust this good advice.

來自字首為 P 的建議

有很多好的建議，是字母 P 開頭的。首先，不要干涉並打擾別人。不要竊取不是你的東西。此外，不要延期或拖延。不要反覆灌輸你相信的事。當你沒有資訊時，不要假裝你有。此外，不要激怒或挑釁別人。不要用拳頭打人。不要使人困惑。最後，不要盜用你沒有付錢購買的資料。要信任這些很好的建議。

P

IV. 填空：

First of all, don't ___1___ into others' business. Don't ___2___ valuable things from others. Don't ___3___ important meetings.

Likewise, don't be a person who ___4___. Don't ___5___ to be honest when you're not. Don't antagonize or ___6___ others.

Remember, it's a crime to ___7___ or hit others. Don't be a ___8___ and odd person. Finally, don't ___9___ content from the Internet.

首先，不要干涉別人的事。不要竊取別人珍貴的東西。重要的會議不要延期。

同樣地，不要做一個喜歡講道理的人。不要假裝誠實。不要與人為敵或激怒他們。

要記得，用拳頭打人是犯罪。不要做一個令人費解又奇怪的人。最後，不要盜用網路上的內容。

【解答】 1. poke　2. poach　3. postpone　4. preaches
5. pretend　6. provoke　7. punch　8. puzzling
9. pirate

* antagonize〔æn'tægə,naɪz〕*v.* 與…為敵
odd〔ɑd〕*adj.* 奇怪的

V. 詞彙題：

Directions: Choose the one word that best completes the sentence.

1. Don't _____ your nose into matters that don't concern you.
   (A) prohibit   (B) protect   (C) permit   (D) poke

2. _____ from others is a sign of weakness and a lack of intelligence.
   (A) Poaching   (B) Persisting   (C) Perceiving   (D) Polishing

3. You can _____ unpleasant events, but you'll eventually have to face them.
   (A) purchase   (B) postpone   (C) paralyze   (D) persevere

4. Please stop your _____. I don't need a lecture.
   (A) packing   (B) pitching   (C) preaching   (D) patrolling

5. There's only so long you can _____ to be something you're not.
   (A) perish   (B) publish   (C) pierce   (D) pretend

6. If you _____ someone, you better be ready to fight.
   (A) preserve   (B) pardon   (C) provoke   (D) promote

7. Watch what you say, or you might get _____ in the face.
   (A) participated   (B) punched   (C) prepared   (D) preferred

8. His behavior that night _____ me for a long time.
   (A) proceeded   (B) populated   (C) prospered   (D) puzzled

9. _____ content from the Internet is illegal.
   (A) Pirating   (B) Punishing   (C) Persuading   (D) Predicting

【答案】 1.（D） 2.（A） 3.（B） 4.（C） 5.（D） 6.（C）
7.（B） 8.（D） 9.（A）

VI. 同義字整理：

1. **poke** 〔 pok 〕 *v.* ①刺；戳 ②干涉

① $\begin{cases} = \text{jab} 〔 dʒæb 〕 \\ = \text{stab} 〔 stæb 〕 \\ = \text{thrust} 〔 θrʌst 〕 \end{cases}$

② $\begin{cases} = \text{meddle} 〔 'mɛdl̩ 〕 \\ = \text{intrude} 〔 ɪn'trud 〕 \end{cases}$

2. **poach** 〔 potʃ 〕 *v.* 偷獵；竊取

$\begin{cases} = \text{steal} 〔 stil 〕 \\ = \text{rob} 〔 rɑb 〕 \\ = \text{plunder} 〔 'plʌndɚ 〕 \end{cases}$

3. **postpone** 〔 post'pon 〕 *v.* 延期

$\begin{cases} = \text{delay} 〔 dɪ'le 〕 \\ = \text{suspend} 〔 sə'spɛnd 〕 \\ = \text{defer} 〔 dɪ'fɝ 〕 \\ = \text{put off} \end{cases}$

4. **preach** 〔 pritʃ 〕 *v.* 說教

$\begin{cases} = \text{lecture} 〔 'lɛktʃɚ 〕 \\ = \text{admonish} 〔 əd'mɑnɪʃ 〕 \\ = \text{sermonize} 〔 's3mən,aɪz 〕 \\ = \text{proclaim} 〔 pro'klem 〕 \end{cases}$

5. **pretend** 〔 prɪ'tɛnd 〕 *v.* 假裝

$\begin{cases} = \text{fake} 〔 fek 〕 \\ = \text{falsify} 〔 'fɔlsə,faɪ 〕 \end{cases}$

$\begin{cases} = \text{feign} 〔 fen 〕 \\ = \text{allege} 〔 ə'lɛdʒ 〕 \end{cases}$

6. **provoke** 〔 prə'vok 〕 *v.* 激怒

$\begin{cases} = \text{anger} 〔 'æŋgɚ 〕 \\ = \text{annoy} 〔 ə'nɔɪ 〕 \\ = \text{offend} 〔 ə'fɛnd 〕 \\ = \text{get on } one's \text{ nerves} \end{cases}$

7. **punch** 〔 pʌntʃ 〕 *v.* 用拳頭打

$\begin{cases} = \text{hit} 〔 hɪt 〕 \\ = \text{strike} 〔 straɪk 〕 \\ = \text{box} 〔 bɑks 〕 \\ = \text{smash} 〔 smæʃ 〕 \end{cases}$

8. **puzzle** 〔 'pʌzl̩ 〕 *v.* 使困惑

$\begin{cases} = \text{perplex} 〔 pɚ'plɛks 〕 \\ = \text{confuse} 〔 kən'fjuz 〕 \\ = \text{baffle} 〔 'bæfl̩ 〕 \\ = \text{bewilder} 〔 bɪ'wɪldɚ 〕 \end{cases}$

9. **pirate** 〔 'paɪrət 〕 *v.* 盜版

$\begin{cases} = \text{copy} 〔 'kɑpɪ 〕 \\ = \text{steal} 〔 stil 〕 \\ = \text{reproduce} 〔 ,riprə'djus 〕 \end{cases}$

$\begin{cases} = \text{poach} 〔 potʃ 〕 \\ = \text{plagiarize} 〔 'pledʒə,raɪz 〕 \end{cases}$

Good Advice: What Not to Do

19. **R (1)**

看英文唸出中文	一口氣說九句	看中文唸出英文

refuse[2]
〔 rɪ'fjuz 〕 *v.*

refute[5]
〔 rɪ'fjut 〕 *v.*

rebel[4]
〔 rɪ'bɛl 〕 *v.*

字首是 refu

Don't *refuse*.
不要拒絕。

Refute.
不要反駁。

Rebel.
不要反叛。

拒絕

反駁

反叛

R

---

restrict[3]
〔 rɪ'strɪkt 〕 *v.*

restrain[5]
〔 rɪ'stren 〕 *v.*

repress[6]
〔 rɪ'prɛs 〕 *v.*

三個是同義字

Restrict.
不要限制別人。

Restrain.
不要限制別人。

Repress.
不要壓制別人。

限制

限制

壓制

---

ridicule[6]
〔'rɪdɪ͵kjul 〕 *v.*

retaliate[6]
〔 rɪ'tælɪ͵et 〕 *v.*

revenge[4]
〔 rɪ'vɛndʒ 〕 *n. v.*

是同義字

Ridicule.
不要嘲笑。

Retaliate.
不要報復。

Seek *revenge*.
不要想報仇。

嘲笑

報復；報仇

報仇

I. 背景説明：

Don't refuse. 可説成：*Don't refuse* to cooperate.（不要拒絕合作。）*Don't refuse* a reasonable request.（不要拒絕合理的要求。）*Refute.* 在此指 Don't *refute*.（不要反駁。）Don't *refute* others.（不要反駁別人。）Don't *refute* the truth.（不要反駁事實。）*Rebel.* 在此指 Don't *rebel*.（不要反叛。）Don't *rebel* against authority.（不要反抗上級。）(=*Don't resist superiors.*) Don't *rebel* against the system.（不要反抗體制。）(=*Don't resist the rules.*) rebel 的意思有：①反叛；造反②反對；不服從；抗命。

Restrict. 在此指 Don't *restrict*.（不要限制別人。）Don't *restrict* changes.（不要限制改變。）Don't *restrict* your ambition.（不要限制你的抱負。）*Restrain.* 在此指 Don't *restrain*.（不要限制別人。）(=*Don't restrain others.*) Don't *restrain* yourself.（不要限制自己。）Don't be *restrained*.（不要被限制。）*Repress.* 在此指 Don't *repress*.（不要壓制別人。）(=*Don't repress others.*) Don't *repress* yourself.（不要壓抑自己。）(=*Don't hold yourself back.*)

Ridicule. 在此指 Don't *ridicule*.（不要嘲笑。）Don't *ridicule* others.（不要嘲笑別人。）(=*Don't make fun of others.*) Don't allow yourself to be *ridiculed*.（不要讓自己被嘲笑。）*Retaliate.* 在此指 Don't *retaliate*.（不要報復。）*Retaliate* only when necessary.（只在有必要的時候才報復。）Don't *relatiate* if you've been wrongly attacked.（如果你被錯誤地攻擊，不要報復。）Seek *revenge*. 在此指 Don't *seek revenge*.（不要想報仇。）Don't try to get *revenge* on your enemies.（不要想對你的敵人報仇。）

II. 英語演講：

【一字英語演講】 【短篇英語演講】

Friends, let me make a few suggestions:

Friends, let me make a few suggestions:
朋友們，讓我提出一些建議：

Don't refuse.
Refute.
Rebel.

Don't refuse to cooperate. 不要拒絕合作。
Don't *refute* the truth. 不要反駁事實。
Don't *rebel* against authority. 不要反抗上級。

Restrict.
Restrain.
Repress.

Don't *restrict* your ambition. 不要限制你的抱負。
Don't be *restrained*. 不要被限制。
Don't *repress* others. 不要壓制別人。

Ridicule.
Retaliate.
Seek revenge.

Don't allow yourself to be *ridiculed*.
不要讓自己被嘲笑。
Don't *retaliate* if you've been wrongly attacked.
如果你被錯誤地攻擊，不要報復。
Don't *seek revenge*. 不要想去報仇。

I hope you appreciate my suggestions.

I hope you appreciate my suggestions.
我希望你們能重視我的建議。

III. 短篇作文：

Suggestions

The following are some helpful suggestions. *To begin with*, *don't refuse* a reasonable request. Don't *refute* others. *Likewise*, don't *rebel* against the system. Don't *restrict* changes. Don't *restrain* yourself. *More importantly*, don't *repress* yourself. And the best suggestion of all is don't *ridicule* or mock people. *Retaliate* only when necessary. Don't try to get *revenge* on your enemies.

建 議

以下是一些有用的建議。首先,不要拒絕合理的要求。不要反駁別人。同樣地,不要反抗體制。不要限制改變。不要限制自己。更重要的是,不要壓抑自己。而最好的建議,就是不要嘲笑別人。只有在必要的時候才報復。不要設法對你的敵人報仇。

IV. 填空:

In the first place, don't ___1___ to cooperate. Don't ___2___ the truth. Don't ___3___ against authority.

Additionally, don't ___4___ your ambition. Don't be a ___5___ person who doesn't show emotion. Don't try to ___6___ others.

Moreover, don't allow yourself to be ___7___. Don't ___8___ if you've been wrongly attacked. Don't seek ___9___.

首先,不要拒絕合作。不要反駁事實。不要反抗上級。

此外,不要限制你的抱負。不要做一個不會表達情緒,拘謹的人。不要想壓制別人。

而且,不要讓自己被嘲笑。如果你被錯誤地攻擊,不要報復。不要想報仇。

【**解答**】 1. refuse　2. refute　3. rebel　4. restrict
　　　　　5. restrained　6. repress　7. ridiculed
　　　　　8. retaliate　9. revenge

* ***in the first place*** 首先
cooperate〔koˊɑpəˌret〕v. 合作
emotion〔ɪˊmoʃən〕n. 情緒

V. 詞彙題：

Directions: Choose the one word that best completes the sentence.

1. Try not to _____ a reasonable request.
   (A) refuse   (B) rattle   (C) relieve   (D) range

2. Don't go out of your way to _____ somebody, even if they're wrong.
   (A) react   (B) refute   (C) realize   (D) raise

3. Those who _____ against the system are doomed to be crushed.
   (A) recall   (B) refine   (C) reduce   (D) rebel

R

4. Don't _____ your mind from wandering to fantastic places.
   (A) rust   (B) restrict   (C) relate   (D) recite

5. Let people be who they are and don't try to _____ them.
   (A) refund   (B) recognize   (C) restrain   (D) refresh

6. _____ your emotions will lead to psychological problems.
   (A) Reaching   (B) Referring   (C) Reminding
   (D) Repressing

7. Take a look in the mirror before you _____ others.
   (A) remain   (B) recruit   (C) regret   (D) ridicule

8. It takes a strong person not to _____ when he's been harmed.
   (A) retaliate   (B) rehearse   (C) recommend   (D) reform

9. Seeking _____ never leads to a peaceful resolution.
   (A) rage   (B) ridge   (C) revenge   (D) ravage

【答案】1.(A) 2.(B) 3.(D) 4.(B) 5.(C) 6.(D)
　　　 7.(D) 8.(A) 9.(C)

VI. 同義字整理：

1. **refuse** (rɪˈfjuz) *v.* 拒絕

   = decline (dɪˈklaɪn)
   = reject (rɪˈdʒɛkt)
   = turn down
   = say no to

2. **refute** (rɪˈfjut) *v.* 反駁

   = disprove (dɪsˈpruv)
   = counter (ˈkaʊntɚ)
   = discredit (dɪsˈkrɛdɪt)
   = prove false

3. **rebel** (rɪˈbɛl) *v.* 反叛

   = revolt (rɪˈvolt)
   = resist (rɪˈzɪst)
   = defy (dɪˈfaɪ)
   = disobey (ˌdɪsəˈbe)

4. **restrict** (rɪˈstrɪkt) *v.* 限制

   = suppress (səˈprɛs)
   = oppress (əˈprɛs)

   = restrain (rɪˈstren)
   = control (kənˈtrol)
   = hold back

5. **restrain** (rɪˈstren) *v.* 限制

   = control (kənˈtrol)
   = restrict (rɪˈstrɪkt)

   = repress (rɪˈprɛs)
   = suppress (səˈprɛs)
   = hold back

6. **repress** (rɪˈprɛs) *v.* 壓制

   = limit (ˈlɪmɪt)
   = restrain (rɪˈstren)
   = regulate (ˈrɛgjəˌlet)
   = curb (kɝb)

7. **ridicule** (ˈrɪdɪˌkjul) *v.* 嘲笑

   = mock (mɑk)
   = taunt (tɔnt)
   = laugh at
   = make fun of

8. **retaliate** (rɪˈtælɪˌet) *v.* 報復；報仇

   = take revenge
   = pay *sb.* back
   = get back at *sb.*
   = get even with

9. **revenge** (rɪˈvɛndʒ) *n. v.* 報仇

   = vengeance (ˈvɛndʒəns)
   = retaliation (rɪˌtælɪˈeʃən)
   = an eye for an eye

R

Good Advice: What Not to Do

20. R (2)

看英文唸出中文	一口氣說九句	看中文唸出英文

ragged[5]

(ˋræɡɪd) *adj.*

字首是 ra

Don't be ***ragged***.
不要穿得邋邋遢遢。

破爛的

rash[6]

(ræʃ) *adj.*

Rash.
不要輕率。

輕率的

是同義字

reckless[5]

(ˋrɛklɪs) *adj.*

Reckless.
不要魯莽。

魯莽的

---

rigid[5]

(ˋrɪdʒɪd) *adj.*

字首是 Ri

Rigid.
不要太嚴格。

嚴格的

ridiculous[5]

(rɪˋdɪkjələs) *adj.*

Ridiculous.
不要太荒謬。

荒謬的

reluctant[4]

(rɪˋlʌktənt) *adj.*

Reluctant.
不要不情願。

不情願的

---

rough[3]

(rʌf) *adj.*

字首是 Ro

Rough.
不要粗魯。

粗糙的

rotten[3]

(ˋrɑtn̩) *adj.*

Rotten.
不要做爛人。

腐爛的

rascal[5]

(ˋræskḷ) *n.*

A ***rascal***.
不要當流氓。

流氓

I. 背景説明 :

  Don't be ragged. (不要穿得邋邋遢遢。) (= *Don't be untidy.*) Don't have a ***ragged*** appearance. (外表不要太邋遢。) 可加強語氣説成 : Don't be ***ragged*** and sloppy.

(不要穿得破破爛爛,邋邋遢遢。)【sloppy〔'slɑpɪ〕*adj.* 邋遢的】***Rash.*** 在此指 Don't be ***rash***. (不要輕率。) Don't make a ***rash*** decision. (不要做輕率的決定。) rash 的意思

> **Don't be ragged.**
> (不要太邋遢。)

有 : ①輕率的 (= *hasty*) ②魯莽的 (= *reckless*)。***Reckless.*** 在此指 Don't be ***reckless***. (不要魯莽。) (= *Don't be a reckless person.*) Don't make ***reckless*** choices. (不要做魯莽的選擇。) Don't be a ***reckless*** driver. (開車不要魯莽。)

  Rigid. 在此指 Don't be ***rigid***. (不要太嚴格。) (= *Don't be strict. = Don't be severe.*) 可加強語氣説成 : Don't be ***rigid*** and inflexible. (不要太嚴格,沒有彈性。) Don't be ***rigid*** and stiff. (不要太嚴格,硬梆梆。)【stiff〔stɪf〕*adj.* 僵硬的】***Ridiculous.*** 在此指 Don't be ***ridiculous***. (不要太荒謬。) Don't be ***ridiculous*** or silly. (不要荒謬或愚蠢。)

> 【比較】 ridicule〔'rɪdɪ,kjul〕*v.* 嘲笑
>
>   ridiculous〔rɪ'dɪkjələs〕*adj.* 荒謬的;可笑的

Reluctant. 在此指 Don't be *reluctant*. (不要心不甘情不願。) Don't be *reluctant* to speak out. (不要不情願大膽地說出來。) (= *Don't be hesitant to speak out*.) Don't be *reluctant* to try new things. (不要不情願嘗試新的事物。) reluctant 的意思有:「不情願的;不願意的;勉強的」。

    Rough. 在此指 Don't be *rough*. (不要粗魯。) 可加強語氣説成:Don't be *rough* and uncivilized. (不要粗魯,不文明。) Don't treat people *roughly*. (不要粗魯地對待別人。) rough 的主要意思是「粗糙的」,可引申爲「粗魯的;粗暴的;粗野的」,都含有「粗」字。*Rotten*. 在此指 Don't be *rotten*. (不要做個爛人。) (= *Don't be a bad person*.) Don't be a *rotten* person. (不要做個爛人。) Don't have a *rotten* attitude. (不要有讓人討厭的態度。) rotten 的主要意思是「腐爛的」,美國人用這個字有幽默感,如 What a *rotten* day! (好爛的天氣!) rotten 表示「壞的」(= *bad*)、「邪惡的」(= *evil*)、「討人厭的」(= *unpleasant*)、「卑劣的」(= *mean*)。A rascal. 在此指 Don't be *a rascal*. (不要當流氓。) Don't behave like *a rascal*. (行爲舉止不要像流氓。) (= *Don't act like a rascal*.) Nobody likes *a rascal*. (沒有人喜歡流氓。)

R

II. 英語演講：

【一字英語演講】

Welcome everybody to my talk:

Don't be ragged.
Rash.
Reckless.

Rigid.
Ridiculous.
Reluctant.

Rough.
Rotten.
A rascal.

Sounds like solid advice, doesn't it?

【短篇英語演講】

Welcome everybody to my talk:
歡迎大家來聽我演講：

Don't be ragged and sloppy.
不要穿得破破爛爛，邋邋遢遢。
Don't make a *rash* decision. 不要做輕率的決定。
Don't be a *reckless* person. 不要做一個魯莽的人。

Don't be *rigid* and inflexible.
不要太嚴格，沒有彈性。
Don't be *ridiculous* or silly. 不要荒謬或愚蠢。
Don't be *reluctant* to speak out.
不要不情願大膽地說出來。

Don't be *rough* and uncivilized.
不要粗魯，不文明。
Don't be a *rotten* person. 不要做個爛人。
Don't behave like *a rascal.* 行為舉止不要像流氓。

Sounds like solid advice, doesn't it?
聽起來像是可靠的建議，不是嗎？

III. 短篇作文：

Solid Advice

We could all use some solid advice. *For starters*, don't have a *ragged* appearance. Don't be a *rash* person. Don't make *reckless* choices. *Additionally*, don't be *rigid* and stiff. Don't be *ridiculous* if you want people to respect you. Don't be *reluctant* to try new things. *Likewise*, don't treat people *roughly*. Don't have a *rotten* attitude. *Above all*, nobody likes a *rascal*. Follow this solid advice and have a nice life.

可靠的建議

　　我們都會想要一些可靠的建議。首先，外表不要太邋遢。不要做一個輕率的人。不要做魯莽的選擇。此外，不要太嚴格，硬梆梆。如果你想要別人尊敬你，不要太荒謬。不要不情願嘗試新的事物。同樣地，不要粗魯地對待別人。不要有讓人討厭的態度。最重要的是，沒有人喜歡流氓。要聽從這些可靠的建議，擁有一個美好的生活。

IV. 填空 :

R

　　Nobody wants to be around a ___1___ and sloppy individual. With that in mind, don't make ___2___ decisions. Don't be a ___3___ and careless person.

　　Furthermore, don't be ___4___ and inflexible. Don't be ___5___ or silly; no one will take you seriously. Don't be ___6___ to try new things.

　　More importantly, don't be a ___7___ and uncivilized character. Don't be a mean and ___8___ person. And finally, don't behave like a ___9___.

　　沒有人會想要在一個穿得破破爛爛，邋邋遢遢的人身邊。考慮到這一點，不要做輕率的決定。不要做一個魯莽又粗心的人。

　　此外，不要太嚴格，沒有彈性。不要荒謬或愚蠢；那樣沒有人會認真看待你。不要不情願嘗試新的事物。

　　更重要的是，不要做一個粗魯又不文明的人。不要做一個卑鄙的爛人。最後，行為舉止不要像流氓。

【解答】 1. ragged　2. rash　3. reckless　4. rigid　5. ridiculous
　　　　　6. reluctant　7. rough　8. rotten　9. rascal

　　* **with…in mind** 考慮到…　　inflexible〔ɪnˈflɛksəbḷ〕*adj.* 沒彈性的
　　　take…seriously 認真看待…
　　　uncivilized〔ʌnˈsɪvḷˌaɪzd〕*adj.* 不文明的　　mean〔min〕*adj.* 卑鄙的

V. 詞彙題：

Directions: *Choose the one word that best completes the sentence.*

1. You won't impress anybody with a _____ appearance.
   (A) rugged   (B) ragged   (C) rapid   (D) radiant

2. _____ decisions always lead to unpleasant outcomes.
   (A) Realistic   (B) Racial   (C) Rash   (D) Rational

3. _____ behavior is a one-way ticket to trouble.
   (A) Reckless   (B) Regular   (C) Responsible   (D) Remarkable

4. A creative person must not be _____ in thought.
   (A) ritual   (B) royal   (C) regional   (D) rigid

5. First, we laugh, and then, we pity a _____ character.
   (A) robust   (B) ridiculous   (C) rainy   (D) reliable

6. If you were _____ to speak up when it mattered, you have no right to complain now.
   (A) raw   (B) radical   (C) reluctant   (D) random

7. You don't have to be _____ with people to get your way.
   (A) recent   (B) rare   (C) rough   (D) residential

8. I know a _____ person when I see one, and I stay as far away as possible.
   (A) rhythmic   (B) remote   (C) respective   (D) rotten

9. Eventually, _____ are brought to justice.
   (A) rascals   (B) radiators   (C) robots   (D) roosters

【答案】1. (B)　2. (C)　3. (A)　4. (D)　5. (B)　6. (C)
　　　　7. (C)　8. (D)　9. (A)

VI. 同義字整理：

1. **ragged**〔'rægɪd〕*adj.* 破爛的

 = worn〔wɔrn〕
 = poor〔pur〕
 = faded〔'fedɪd〕
 = shabby〔'ʃæbɪ〕

2. **rash**〔ræʃ〕*adj.* 輕率的

 = hasty〔'hestɪ〕
 = reckless〔'rɛklɪs〕
 = imprudent〔ɪm'prudn̩t〕
 = impulsive〔ɪm'pʌlsɪv〕

3. **reckless**〔'rɛklɪs〕*adj.* 魯莽的

 = rash〔ræʃ〕
 = hasty〔'hestɪ〕
 = careless〔'kɛrlɪs〕
 = thoughtless〔'θɔtlɪs〕

4. **rigid**〔'rɪdʒɪd〕*adj.* 嚴格的

 = strict〔strɪkt〕
 = harsh〔harʃ〕
 = severe〔sə'vɪr〕
 = rigorous〔'rɪgərəs〕

5. **ridiculous**〔rɪ'dɪkjələs〕*adj.* 荒謬的

 = stupid〔'stjupɪd〕
 = foolish〔'fulɪʃ〕
 = laughable〔'læfəbl̩〕

6. **reluctant**〔rɪ'lʌktənt〕*adj.* 勉強的

 = unwilling〔ʌn'wɪlɪŋ〕
 = hesitant〔'hɛzətənt〕
 = unenthusiastic〔ʌn,ɪnθjuzɪ'æstɪk〕

7. **rough**〔rʌf〕*adj.* 粗糙的；粗魯的

 = rude〔rud〕
 = ungracious〔ʌn'greʃəs〕
 = impolite〔,ɪmpə'laɪt〕
 = ill-mannered〔,ɪl'mænɚd〕

8. **rotten**〔'ratn̩〕*adj.* 腐爛的；墮落的；極壞的

 = mean〔min〕
 = nasty〔'næstɪ〕
 = corrupt〔kə'rʌpt〕

 = wicked〔'wɪkɪd〕
 = immoral〔ɪ'mɔrəl〕

9. **rascal**〔'ræskl̩〕*n.* 流氓

 = villain〔'vɪlən〕
 = rogue〔rog〕
 = bad egg
 = good-for-nothing〔'gud fɚ ,nʌθɪŋ〕

R

Good Advice: What Not to Do

21. S (1)

看英文唸出中文	一口氣說九句	看中文唸出英文
scold[4] 〔 skold 〕 v.	字首都是 sc {	**Don't *scold*.** 不要責罵人。	責罵
scorn[5] 〔 skɔrn 〕 v.		***Scorn*.** 不要輕視人。	輕視
scream[3] 〔 skrim 〕 v.		***Scream*.** 不要尖叫。	尖叫

sneer[6] 〔 snɪr 〕 v.	字首都是 Sn {	***Sneer*.** 不要輕視。	輕視;嘲笑
snort[5] 〔 snɔrt 〕 v.		***Snort*.** 不要哼鼻子。	哼鼻子;輕視
snarl[5] 〔 snɑrl 〕 v.		***Snarl*.** 不要咆哮。	咆哮

shallow[3] 〔'ʃælo 〕 adj.	字首是 sha {	**Don't be *shallow*.** 不要膚淺。	淺的
shabby[5] 〔'ʃæbɪ 〕 adj.		***Shabby*.** 不要衣衫襤褸。	衣衫襤褸的
sloppy[5] 〔'slɑpɪ 〕 adj.		***Sloppy*.** 不要邋遢。	邋遢的

I. 背景説明：

　　Don't scold. 可説成：Don't *scold* others. (不要責罵別人。) Nobody likes to be *scolded*. (沒有人喜歡被責罵。) *Scorn*. 在此指 Don't *scorn*. (不要輕視人。)(= *Don't scorn people*.) It's impolite to *scorn* others. (輕視別人不禮貌。) Don't *scorn* others for mistakes. (不要因為錯誤而輕視人。) (= *Don't look down on others for mistakes*.) *Scream*. 在此指 Don't *scream*. (不要尖叫。) Don't yell and *scream* at people. (對別人不要尖聲吼叫。)(= *Don't scream and yell at people*.) Nobody likes a person who is always *screaming*. (沒有人喜歡總是尖叫的人。)

　　Sneer. 在此指 Don't *sneer*. (不要輕視。) Don't *sneer* and look down on people. (不要嘲笑輕視人。) Don't *sneer* at good advice. (不要輕視好的勸告。) sneer 的意思有：「輕視；嘲笑；譏諷」。*Snort*. 在此指 Don't *snort*. (不要哼鼻子。) (= *Don't make a noisy sound like a horse*.) Don't *snort* at good advice. (不要輕視好的勸告。) Don't *snort* at others. (不要輕視別人。)(= *Don't express contempt for others*.) snort 的主要意思是「哼鼻子」。用鼻子發出「哼」的聲音，表示「輕視」。*Snarl*. 在此指 Don't *snarl*. (不要咆哮。) Don't *snarl* at people. (不要對人咆哮。) Don't *snarl* or growl. (不要咆哮或吼叫。) snarl 的意思有：「狂吠；咆哮；吼叫」。snarl〔snɑrl〕這個字不好唸，唸時要加強 /r/ 的發音，像是 Karl〔kɑrl〕*n.* 卡爾。

> **Don't snort.**

S

    Don't be shallow. (= *Don't be a shallow person.*) shallow 的主要意思是「淺的」，引申爲「膚淺的」(= *superficial* = *surface* = *empty*)。Don't be ***shallow*** and vain. (不要膚淺又虛榮。)

    Shabby. 在此指 Don't be ***shabby***. (不要衣衫襤褸。) (= *Don't be neglectful of your appearance.* = *Don't be ragged.*) *Sloppy.* 在此指 Don't be ***sloppy***. (不要邋遢。) (= *Don't be untidy and careless.*) Don't be a ***sloppy*** person. (不要做一個邋遢的人。) Don't live a ***sloppy*** life. (不要過著髒亂的生活。) sloppy 還可作「(衣服) 寬鬆的」解，因爲穿得太寬鬆，就會顯得邋遢，如 a ***sloppy*** sweatshirt (寬鬆的運動服)。

II. 英語演講：

【一字英語演講】	【短篇英語演講】
Great to see all of you here:	*Great to see all of you here:*　很高興在這裡見到大家：
Don't scold.　*Scorn.*　*Scream.*	*Don't scold* others.　不要責罵別人。 Don't *scorn* people.　不要輕視人。 Don't yell and *scream* at people.　對別人不要尖聲吼叫。
Sneer.　*Snort.*　*Snarl.*	Don't *sneer* at good advice.　不要輕視好的勸告。 Don't *snort* at others.　不要輕視別人。 Don't *snarl* at people.　不要對人咆哮。
Don't be shallow.　*Shabby.*　*Sloppy.*	*Don't be* a *shallow* person.　不要做個膚淺的人。 Don't have a *shabby* appearance.　不要有衣衫襤褸的外表。 Don't be a *sloppy* person.　不要做一個邋遢的人。
This is fantastic advice.	*This is fantastic advice*.　這些是很棒的建議。

S

III. 短篇作文：

Fantastic Advice

Do you need some fantastic advice? *First of all*, nobody likes to be *scolded*. It's impolite to *scorn* others. Nobody likes a person who is always *screaming*. *Moreover*, don't *sneer* and look down on people. Don't *snort* at good advice. *And of course*, don't *snarl* and growl like a dog. *On top of that*, *don't be shallow* and vain. Don't be *shabby* and neglectful of your appearance. *But the most fantastic advice of all*: Don't live a *sloppy* life.

很棒的建議

你需要一些很棒的建議嗎？首先，沒有人喜歡被責罵。輕視別人不禮貌。沒有人喜歡總是尖叫的人。而且，不要嘲笑輕視人。不要輕視好的勸告。當然，不要像狗一樣咆哮。此外，不要膚淺又虛榮。不要衣衫襤褸，忽視你的外表。但最棒的建議就是：不要過著髒亂的生活。

* fantastic〔fæn'tæstɪk〕*adj.* 很棒的　　***look down on*** 輕視
　growl〔graʊl〕*v.* 咆哮　　vain〔ven〕*adj.* 虛榮的
　neglectful〔nɪ'glɛktfəl〕*adj.* 忽視的

IV. 填空：

Unless you're a perfect person, you shouldn't ___1___ others. For sure, don't ___2___ people for mistakes. Don't yell and ___3___ at people.

Additionally, don't ___4___ at good advice. Don't ___5___ at others or criticize their ideas. Don't ___6___ at people like an angry dog.

Finally, don't be a ___7___ person. Don't look like a bum with a ___8___ appearance. Don't be a ___9___ person.

除非你是個完美的人，不然你不應該責罵別人。當然，不要因為錯誤而輕視人。對別人不要尖聲吼叫。

此外，不要輕視好的勸告。不要輕視別人，或批評他們的想法。不要像一隻生氣的狗對人咆哮。

最後，不要做一個膚淺的人。不要看起來像個流浪漢，有衣衫襤褸的外表。不要做一個邋遢的人。

【解答】 1. scold　2. scorn　3. scream　4. sneer　5. snort
　　　　 6. snarl　7. shallow　8. shabby　9. sloppy
　　* ***for sure*** 當然　　bum〔bʌm〕*n.* 流浪漢；乞丐

V. 詞彙題：

Directions: Choose the one word that best completes the sentence.

1. Unless you've never made a mistake in your life, don't _____ others.
   (A) subtract   (B) safeguard   (C) scold   (D) scrub

2. If need be, express your _____ for others in private, not in public.
   (A) scope   (B) scorn   (C) scrap   (D) script

3. I can't talk to a person who's always _____ at me.
   (A) submitting   (B) struggling   (C) supplying   (D) screaming

4. _____ is unattractive and rude.
   (A) Sneering   (B) Satisfying   (C) Subscribing   (D) Scrolling

5. Many a fool has _____ at good advice, only to regret it later.
   (A) scratched   (B) scolded   (C) snorted   (D) scooped

6. If you _____ at me, we're going to have a problem.
   (A) scare   (B) snarl   (C) soothe   (D) scan

7. _____ people are as disposable as facial tissues.
   (A) Simultaneous   (B) Scarce   (C) Sensible   (D) Shallow

8. Who wants to get involved with a _____ and neglectful person?
   (A) shrewd   (B) significant   (C) satisfactory   (D) shabby

9. If you're a _____ person, you'd better get your act together.
   (A) sloppy   (B) skillful   (C) sincere   (D) selective

【答案】 1.(C)　2.(B)　3.(D)　4.(A)　5.(C)　6.(B)
　　　　 7.(D)　8.(D)　9.(A)

VI. 同義字整理：

1. **scold** 〔 skold 〕 *v.* 責罵

- = blame 〔 blem 〕
- = lecture 〔'lɛktʃɚ 〕
- = reprimand 〔,rɛprɪ'mænd 〕
- = find fault with

2. **scorn** 〔 skɔrn 〕 *v.* 輕視

- = slight 〔 slaɪt 〕
- = despise 〔 dɪ'spaɪz 〕
- = look down on
- = hold in contempt

3. **scream** 〔 skrim 〕 *v.* 尖叫

- = cry 〔 kraɪ 〕
- = yell 〔 jɛl 〕
- = shriek 〔 ʃrik 〕
- = howl 〔 haʊl 〕

4. **sneer** 〔 snɪr 〕 *v.* 輕視

- = jeer 〔 dʒɪr 〕
- = mock 〔 mak 〕

- = ridicule 〔'rɪdɪ,kjul 〕
- = scorn 〔 skɔrn 〕
- = look down on

5. **snort** 〔 snɔrt 〕 *v.* 哼鼻子；輕視

- = emit 〔 ɪ'mɪt 〕
- = utter 〔'ʌtɚ 〕
- = indicate contempt by breathing noisily and forcefully through the nose

6. **snarl** 〔 snɑrl 〕 *v.* 咆哮

- = growl 〔 graʊl 〕
- = bark 〔 bark 〕
- = speak angrily
- = speak roughly

7. **shallow** 〔'ʃælo 〕 *adj.* 淺的；膚淺的

- = foolish 〔'fulɪʃ 〕
- = empty 〔'ɛmptɪ 〕
- = surface 〔'sɝfɪs 〕
- = superficial 〔,supɚ'fɪʃəl 〕

8. **shabby** 〔'ʃæbɪ 〕 *adj.* 衣衫襤褸的

- = ragged 〔'rægɪd 〕
- = faded 〔'fedɪd 〕
- = worn-out 〔'wɔrn'aʊt 〕
- = tattered 〔'tætɚd 〕

9. **sloppy** 〔'slɑpɪ 〕 *adj.* 邋遢的

- = messy 〔'mɛsɪ 〕
- = untidy 〔 ʌn'taɪdɪ 〕

Good Advice: What Not to Do

22. S (2)

看英文唸出中文	一口氣說九句	看中文唸出英文

shout[1]
〔 ʃaʊt 〕 v.

字首都是 sh

Don't *shout*.
不要吼叫。

吼叫

shrug[4]
〔 ʃrʌg 〕 v.

***Shrug*.**
不要聳肩。

聳肩

shun[6]
〔 ʃʌn 〕 v.

***Shun* others.**
不要躲避別人。

躲避

---

sob[4]
〔 sɑb 〕 v.

***Sob*.**
不要哭哭啼啼。

哭哭啼啼

stammer[6]
〔'stæmə 〕 n. v.

是同義字

***Stammer*.**
不要口吃。

字首是 St

字尾是 er

口吃

stutter[5]
〔'stʌtə 〕 v.

***Stutter*.**
不要口吃。

口吃

---

swear[3]
〔 swɛr 〕 v.

由短到長

***Swear*.**
不要罵髒話。

發誓；咒罵

stumble[5]
〔'stʌmbḷ 〕 v.

***Stumble*.**
不要被絆倒。

絆倒

surrender[4]
〔 sə'rɛndə 〕 v.

***Surrender*.**
不要放棄。

投降；放棄

S

I. 背景說明 :

Don't shout. 可說成 : *Don't shout* at people. (不要對人吼叫。) *Don't* scream and *shout.* (不要尖聲吼叫。) *Shrug.* 在此指 Don't *shrug.* (不要聳肩。) Don't *shrug* at problems. (不要碰到問題就聳肩。) Don't *shrug* when asked a question. (當被問到問題時，不要聳肩。) shrug (聳肩) 表示「不知情或不感興趣」。*Shun others.* 在此指 Don't *shun others.* (不要躲避別人。)(= *Don't avoid a person deliberately.*) Don't *shun* your friends. (不要躲避你的朋友。) Don't *shun* your family. (不要躲避你的家人。)

Sob. 在此指 Don't *sob.* (不要哭哭啼啼。)(= *Don't cry.*) Don't *sob* in public. (不要當眾哭哭啼啼。) Don't let anybody see you *sob.* (不要讓人看到你在哭。) *Stammer.* 在此指 Don't *stammer.* (不要口吃。) Try not to *stammer.* (儘量不要結結巴巴。) Reciting One Word English will cure your *stammering.* (背「英文一字金」可以治療口吃。) Don't be a person that *stammers.* (不要做一個說話結巴的人。) *Stutter.* 在此指 Don't *stutter.* (不要口吃。) Don't *stutter* when you speak. (說話不要結巴。) Don't be a person that *stutters.* (不要做一個說話結巴的人。)

Swear. 在此指 Don't *swear*. (不要罵髒話。)(= *Don't curse.* = *Don't use foul language.* = *Don't say bad words.*) swear 的主要意思是「發誓」，在此作「咒罵；責罵；用髒話罵」解。Don't *swear* at people. (不要用髒話罵人。) Don't *swear* or curse in public. (不要當眾罵髒話。)

Stumble. 在此指 Don't *stumble*. (不要被絆倒。)(= *Don't trip.*) Don't *stumble* over your own feet. (不要被自己的腳絆倒。) 還可引申為「不要害到自己。」(= *Don't sabotage yourself.*)

Surrender. 在此指 Don't *surrender*. (不要放棄。)(= *Don't give up.*) Don't *surrender* your dreams. (不要放棄你的夢想。) Don't *surrender* to bad habits. (不要向壞習慣屈服。) surrender 的主要意思是「投降」，在此作「放棄；屈服」解。

II. 英語演講：

【一字英語演講】	【短篇英語演講】
Friends, I have some news for you:	*Friends, I have some news for you:* 朋友們，我有一些消息要告訴你們：
Don't shout. *Shrug.* *Shun others.*	*Don't shout* at people. 不要對人吼叫。 Don't *shrug* at problems. 不要碰到問題就聳肩。 Don't *shun others*. 不要躲避別人。
Sob. *Stammer.* *Stutter.*	Don't let anybody see you *sob*. 不要讓人看到你在哭。 Reciting One Word English will cure your *stammering*. 背「英文一字金」可以治療口吃。 Don't be a person that *stutters*. 不要做一個說話結巴的人。
Swear. *Stumble.* *Surrender.*	Don't *swear* or curse in public. 不要當眾罵髒話。 Don't *stumble* over your own feet. 不要害到自己。 Don't *surrender* to bad habits. 不要向壞習慣屈服。
This is the best advice I've ever heard.	*This is the best advice I've ever heard.* 這些是我所聽過最好的建議。

S

III. 短篇作文：

The Best Advice I've Ever Heard

The following is the best advice I've ever heard. *First, don't* scream and *shout*. Don't *shrug* when asked a question. And don't *shun* your family. *On top of that*, don't *sob* in public. Don't be a person that *stammers*. *Additionally*, don't *stutter* when you speak. Don't *swear* at people. Don't *stumble* over your own feet. *In the end*, don't *surrender* your dreams and you'll be a happy person. That's the best advice I've ever heard.

我所聽過最好的建議

以下是我所聽過最好的建議。首先，不要尖聲吼叫。當被問到問題時，不要聳肩。而且不要躲避你的家人。此外，不要當眾哭哭啼啼。不要做一個說話結巴的人。而且，說話不要口吃。不要用髒話罵人。不要害到自己。最後，不要放棄你的夢想，那樣你才會快樂。這些就是我所聽過最好的建議。

IV. 填空：

If you ___1___ at people, you're going to have a tough time. Contrarily, don't ___2___ at problems when you could easily solve them. Don't ___3___ your friends.

Meanwhile, don't let anybody see you ___4___. Reciting One Word English will cure your ___5___. Don't be a person that ___6___.

Furthermore, don't ___7___ or curse in public. Don't ___8___ over your own feet. And finally, don't ___9___ to bad habits like smoking or gambling.

如果你對人吼叫，你就會日子不好過。相反地，不要碰到問題就聳肩，那你就能輕易地解決它們。不要躲避你的朋友。

同時，不要讓人看到你在哭。背「英文一字金」可以治療口吃。不要做一個說話結巴的人。

此外，不要當眾罵髒話。不要害到自己。最後，不要向像是抽煙或賭博這樣的壞習慣屈服。

【解答】 1. shout　2. shrug　3. shun　4. sob　5. stammering
　　　　 6. stutters　7. swear　8. stumble　9. surrender

* tough 〔tʌf〕 *adj.* 困難的　　***have a tough time*** 日子不好過

V. 詞彙題 :

Directions: *Choose the one word that best completes the sentence.*

1. You don't win arguments by _____ louder than your opponent.
   (A) seducing　(B) shouting　(C) steering　(D) starving

2. If your response to a problem is to _____, you're a loser.
   (A) seize　(B) settle　(C) shrug　(D) strive

3. You're going to be lonely if you _____ the people who care about you.
   (A) symbolize　(B) sharpen　(C) sympathize　(D) shun

4. Stop _____, grow up, and face your problems like an adult.
   (A) sobbing　(B) startling　(C) spraining　(D) slumping

5. Try saying that again, but this time, don't _____.
   (A) simmer　(B) stammer　(C) sketch　(D) squeeze

6. I didn't understand what you said because you were _____.
   (A) slamming　(B) shutting　(C) stuttering　(D) shifting

7. Don't _____ in front of young children.
   (A) swear　(B) shrink　(C) simplify　(D) support

8. If you _____ and fall, pick yourself up and keep going.
   (A) suppose　(B) specialize　(C) summon　(D) stumble

9. Fight as hard as you can and refuse to _____.
   (A) straighten　(B) socialize　(C) suggest　(D) surrender

【答案】 1. (B)　2. (C)　3. (D)　4. (A)　5. (B)　6. (C)
　　　　 7. (A)　8. (D)　9. (D)

VI. 同義字整理：

1. **shout** 〔 ʃaʊt 〕 *v.* 吼叫

> = cry 〔 kraɪ 〕
> = yell 〔 jɛl 〕
> = scream 〔 skrim 〕
> = roar 〔 ror 〕

2. **shrug** 〔 ʃrʌg 〕 *v.* 聳肩

> = brush aside
> = shrug off
> = raise *one's* shoulders to indicate indifference or resignation

3. **shun** 〔 ʃʌn 〕 *v.* 躲避

> = avoid 〔 ə'vɔɪd 〕
> = evade 〔 ɪ'ved 〕
> = keep away from

4. **sob** 〔 sab 〕 *v.* 哭哭啼啼

> = cry 〔 kraɪ 〕
> = weep 〔 wip 〕
> = shed tears

5. **stammer** 〔 'stæmɚ 〕 *n. v.* 口吃

> = stutter 〔 'stʌtɚ 〕
> = falter 〔 'fɔltɚ 〕
> = hesitate 〔 'hɛzə,tet 〕
> = stumble over *one's* words

6. **stutter** 〔 'stʌtɚ 〕 *v.* 口吃

> = stammer 〔 'stæmɚ 〕
> = stumble 〔 'stʌmbl̩ 〕

> = falter 〔 'fɔltɚ 〕
> = hesitate 〔 'hɛzə,tet 〕
> = speak haltingly

7. **swear** 〔 swɛr 〕 *v.* 發誓；咒罵

> = curse 〔 kɝs 〕
> = be foul-mouthed
> = utter profanities

8. **stumble** 〔 'stʌmbl̩ 〕 *v.* 絆倒

> = trip 〔 trɪp 〕
> = fall 〔 fɔl 〕

> = falter 〔 'fɔltɚ 〕
> = stagger 〔 'stægɚ 〕
> = lose *one's* balance

9. **surrender** 〔 sə'rɛndɚ 〕 *v.* 投降；屈服；放棄

> = yield 〔 jild 〕
> = quit 〔 kwɪt 〕

> = submit 〔 səb'mɪt 〕
> = succumb 〔 sə'kʌm 〕

> = give in
> = give up

Good Advice: What Not to Do

23. T

看英文唸出中文	一口氣說九句	看中文唸出英文

tease³
〔 tiz 〕*v.*

是同義字 { **Don't *tease*.**
不要取笑。

取笑

taunt⁵
〔 tɔnt 〕*v.*

***Taunt*.**
不要嘲笑。

嘲笑

threaten³
〔'θrɛtn̩〕*v.*

***Threaten*.**
不要威脅。

威脅

---

trip¹
〔 trɪp 〕*v.*

句意相關 { ***Trip*.**
不要被絆倒。

絆倒

tumble³
〔'tʌmbl̩〕*v.*

***Tumble*.**
不要跌倒。

跌倒

twist³
〔 twɪst 〕*v.*

***Twist*.**
不要扭傷。

扭傷；扭曲

---

tense⁴
〔 tɛns 〕*adj.*

句意相關 { **Don't be *tense*.**
不要緊張。

緊張的

timid⁴
〔'tɪmɪd〕*adj.*

***Timid*.**
不要膽小。

膽小的

tedious⁶
〔'tidɪəs〕*adj.*

***Tedious*.**
不要讓人討厭。

乏味的

I. 背景說明：

Don't tease. 可說成：*Don't tease* others.（不要取笑別人。）
（= *Don't make fun of others.*）*Teasing* makes people uncomfortable.
（冷嘲熱諷會讓人不舒服。）*Taunt.* 在此指 Don't *taunt.*（不要嘲笑。）
Don't *taunt* people.（不要嘲笑人。）Don't *taunt* your enemies.（不
要嘲笑你的敵人。）*Threaten.* 在此指 Don't *threaten.*（不要威脅。）
Don't *threaten* people.（不要威脅人。）Never *threaten* people with
violence.（永遠不要用暴力威脅人。）

Trip. 在此指 Don't *trip.*（不要被絆倒。）（= *Don't stumble.*）
Don't *trip* and fall.（不要被絆倒。）Don't get *tripped* up.（不要被絆
倒。）（= *Don't get tripped.*）trip 的主要意思是「旅行」，在此作「絆
倒」解。*Tumble.* 在此指 Don't *tumble.*（不要跌倒。）（= *Don't fall
down.*）Be careful or you'll *tumble.*（要小心，否則你就會跌倒。）
Don't *tumble* and fall.（不要跌倒。）*Twist.* 在此指 Don't *twist.*（不
要扭傷。）Don't tumble, or you may *twist* your ankle.（不要跌倒，
否則可能會扭傷腳踝。）萬一扭傷了腳，前 12 小時要冰敷，後 12 小時
要熱敷，並吃消炎、消腫藥即可。twist 也可作「扭曲」解。Don't
twist people's words.（不要曲解別人說的話。）Don't *twist* the
truth.（不要扭曲事實。）（= *Don't distort the truth.*）

Don't be tense. 可說成：*Don't be* a *tense* person.（不要做個緊
張的人。）*Don't be tense* and anxious.（不要緊張焦慮。）*Timid.* 在
此指 Don't be *timid.*（不要膽小。）（= *Don't be a timid person.*）Don't
be *timid* and shy.（不要膽小害羞。）*Tedious.* 在此指 Don't be
tedious.（不要讓人討厭。）（= *Don't be unpleasant.*）Don't talk
about *tedious* subjects.（不要談論無聊的話題。）tedious 的意思有：
「單調乏味的；令人生厭的；冗長的；囉嗦的」。

II. 英語演講：

【一字英語演講】　　【短篇英語演講】

Here are nine short pieces of good advice:	*Here are nine short pieces of good advice:* 以下有九個簡短的好建議：
	Don't tease others. 不要取笑別人。
Don't tease.	Don't *taunt* your enemies.
Taunt.	不要嘲笑你的敵人。
Threaten.	Don't *threaten* people. 不要威脅人。
Trip.	Don't *trip* and fall. 不要被絆倒。
Tumble.	Don't *tumble* and fall. 不要跌倒。
Twist.	Don't *twist*. 不要扭傷。
Don't be tense.	*Don't be* a *tense* person. 不要做個緊張的人。
Timid.	Don't be *timid* and shy. 不要膽小害羞。
Tedious.	Don't talk about *tedious* subjects. 不要談論無聊的話題。
I hope you enjoyed my speech.	*I hope you enjoyed my speech.* 我希望你們喜歡我的演講。

III. 短篇作文：

Nine Short Pieces of Good Advice

Have a look at these nine short pieces of good advice. One: *Teasing* makes people uncomfortable. Two: Don't *taunt* people. Three: Never *threaten* people with violence. Four: Don't get *tripped* up. Five: Be careful or you'll *tumble*. Six: Don't *twist*. Seven: *Don't be tense* and anxious. Eight: Don't be a *timid* person. *And last but not least*: Don't be a *tedious* person.

九個簡短的好建議

要看一看這九個簡短的好建議。第一：冷嘲熱諷會讓人不舒服。第二：不要嘲笑人。第三：永遠不要用暴力威脅人。第四：不要被絆倒。第五：要小心，否則你就會跌倒。第六：不要扭傷。第七：不要緊張焦慮。第八：不要做一個膽小的人。最後一項要點是：不要讓人討厭。

* violence〔ˋvaɪələns〕*n.* 暴力　　anxious〔ˋæŋkʃəs〕*adj.* 焦慮的
last but not least 最後一項要點是

IV. 填空：

Don't ___1___ and make fun of others. Moreover, don't ___2___ your enemies unless you're ready for a fight. Don't ___3___ to harm people.

In a similar fashion, don't ___4___ and fall to the ground. Don't ___5___ and hurt yourself. Don't ___6___.

To sum up, don't be a ___7___ person. Don't be a ___8___ and shy character. Don't talk about dreary and ___9___ subjects.

不要取笑別人。此外，不要嘲笑你的敵人，除非你準備要打架。不要威脅要傷害別人。

同樣地，不要被絆倒。不要跌倒，使自己受傷。不要扭傷。

總之，不要做個緊張的人。不要做個膽小又害羞的人。不要談論非常無聊的話題。

【解答】 1. tease　2. taunt　3. threaten　4. trip　5. tumble
　　　　 6. twist　7. tense　8. timid　9. tedious

* ***make fun of*** 取笑　　fashion〔ˋfæʃən〕*n.* 方式
in a similar fashion 同樣地（= *similarly*）
to sum up 總之　　dreary〔ˋdrɪrɪ〕*adj.* 無聊的；乏味的

V. 詞彙題：

Directions: *Choose the one word that best completes the sentence.*

1. You're going to be sorry if you keep _____ people.
   (A) trembling (B) teasing (C) trespassing (D) translating

2. If you _____ me, I'm going to respond in a very unpleasant way.
   (A) treasure (B) tremble (C) taunt (D) transform

3. Don't _____ to do something; just do it.
   (A) trample (B) threaten (C) tangle (D) terminate

4. Watch where you are going so you don't _____.
   (A) trip (B) trim (C) torture (D) transfer

5. If you're not paying attention, you're going to _____.
   (A) twinkle (B) tolerate (C) tumble (D) tackle

6. I don't trust a person who _____ my words.
   (A) triggers (B) tightens (C) terrifies (D) twists

7. Try not to be so _____ — relax.
   (A) tolerable (B) tentative (C) typical (D) tense

8. It's easy to take advantage of a _____ person.
   (A) timid (B) theoretical (C) thorough (D) temporary

9. Don't get a reputation for being _____ and tiresome.
   (A) toxic (B) tedious (C) terminal (D) thoughtful

【答案】1.（B） 2.（C） 3.（B） 4.（A） 5.（C） 6.（D）
　　　　7.（D） 8.（A） 9.（B）

VI. 同義字整理：

1. tease 〔 tiz 〕 *v.* 取笑

= taunt 〔 tɔnt 〕
= mock 〔 mɑk 〕
= ridicule 〔 'rɪdɪ,kjul 〕

2. taunt 〔 tɔnt 〕 *v.* 嘲笑

= mock 〔 mɑk 〕
= jeer 〔 dʒɪr 〕
= sneer 〔 snɪr 〕

= tease 〔 tiz 〕
= ridicule 〔 'rɪdɪ,kjul 〕

3. threaten 〔 'θrɛtn̩ 〕 *v.* 威脅

= warn 〔 wɔrn 〕
= bully 〔 'bʊlɪ 〕
= terrorize 〔 'tɛrə,raɪz 〕
= intimidate 〔 ɪn'tɪmə,det 〕

4. trip 〔 trɪp 〕 *v.* 絆倒

= fall 〔 fɔl 〕
= stumble 〔 'stʌmbl̩ 〕
= tumble 〔 'tʌmbl̩ 〕

= stagger 〔 'stægɚ 〕
= lose *one's* balance

5. tumble 〔 'tʌmbl̩ 〕 *v.* 跌倒

= fall 〔 fɔl 〕
= drop 〔 drɑp 〕
= trip up
= stumble 〔 'stʌmbl̩ 〕

6. twist 〔 twɪst 〕 *v.* 扭傷；扭曲

① = sprain 〔 spren 〕
= wrench 〔 rɛntʃ 〕

② = distort 〔 dɪs'tɔrt 〕
= misrepresent 〔 mɪs,rɛprɪ'zɛnt 〕

7. tense 〔 tɛns 〕 *adj.* 緊張的

= nervous 〔 'nɝvəs 〕
= anxious 〔 'æŋkʃəs 〕

= stressful 〔 'strɛsfəl 〕
= strained 〔 strend 〕
= under pressure

8. timid 〔 'tɪmɪd 〕 *adj.* 膽小的

= shy 〔 ʃaɪ 〕
= fearful 〔 'fɪrfəl 〕
= cowardly 〔 'kaʊwɚdlɪ 〕

9. tedious 〔 'tidɪəs 〕 *adj.* 乏味的

= dull 〔 dʌl 〕
= boring 〔 'borɪŋ 〕
= monotonous 〔 mə'nɑtn̩əs 〕
= uninteresting 〔 ʌn'ɪntrɪstɪŋ 〕

Good Advice: What Not to Do

24. U , V , W

看英文唸出中文	一口氣説九句	看中文唸出英文

undermine[6]
(͵ʌndɚˈmaɪn) *v.*

Don't **undermine** others.
不要暗中害人。

字首都是 u / 字首是 under

損害

underestimate[6]
(͵ʌndɚˈɛstə͵met) *v.*

Underestimate people. 不要低估別人。

低估

upset[3]
(ʌpˈsɛt) *adj.*

Be **upset**.
不要不高興。

不高興的

----

vague[5]
(veg) *adj.*

Don't be **vague**.
不要說話模糊。

字首都是 v / 字首是 Vi

模糊的

vicious[6]
(ˈvɪʃəs) *adj.*

Vicious.
不要有壞心眼。

邪惡的

violent[3]
(ˈvaɪələnt) *adj.*

Violent.
不要有暴力傾向。

暴力的

----

weak[1]
(wik) *adj.*

Weak.
不要軟弱。

字首都是 W / 字首是 We

虛弱的

weird[5]
(wɪrd) *adj.*

Weird.
不要怪裡怪氣。

奇怪的

wicked[3]
(ˈwɪkɪd) *adj.*

Wicked.
不要當壞人。

邪惡的

I. 背景說明：

Don't undermine others. (= *Don't hurt others.*) 可説成：
Don't ***undermine*** yourself. (不要害自己。) (= *Don't hurt yourself.*) Don't ***undermine*** your friends. (不要暗中害朋友。)
undermine 的字面意思是「在…底下挖」，under (在…之下)
+ mine (挖礦)，引申為「損害；暗中破壞」。*Underestimate people.* 在此指 ***Don't underestimate*** people. (不要低估別人。) 可説成：***Don't underestimate*** things. (不要低估事情。)
Don't underestimate your enemies. (不要低估你的敵人。)
underestimate 是由 under (在…之下) + estimate (估計) 組成。*Be upset.* 在此指 Don't be ***upset***. (不要不高興。) Don't be easily ***upset***. (不要容易生氣。) Don't get ***upset*** and lose your cool. (不要生氣，失去冷靜。) upset 可作「不高興的；生氣的」解。【*lose your cool* 發火；失去冷靜】

Don't be vague. 可説成：Don't make ***vague*** statements. (不要說不清楚。) Don't be a ***vague*** person. (不要做一個說話含糊的人。) (= *Don't be a person who does not express himself clearly.*)【現代英文可用 themselves 代替 himself】
Vicious. 在此指 Don't be ***vicious***. (不要有壞心眼。) (= *Don't be a vicious person.*) Don't engage in ***vicious*** behavior. (不要做壞事。) (= *Don't do malicious things.*) Don't be ***vicious*** and cruel. (不要邪惡又殘忍。) *Violent.* 在此指 Don't be ***violent***. (不要有暴力傾向。) (= *Don't be a violent person.*)
Don't be ***violent*** toward others. (不要對他人粗暴。)

U

Weak. 在此指 Don't be *weak*. (不要軟弱。) (= *Don't be a weak person.*) Don't be *weak* and incapable. (不要軟弱無能。) *Weird*. 在此指 Don't be *weird*. (不要怪裡怪氣。) Don't be a *weird* person. (不要當怪人。) Don't talk about *weird* things. (不要談論奇怪的事。) *Wicked*. 在此指 Don't be *wicked*. (不要當壞人。) (= *Don't be a wicked person.*) Don't have a *wicked* character. (不要有壞的個性。) Avoid *wicked* people. (要避開壞人。)

Hey guys:

Don't undermine others.
Underestimate people.
Be upset.

Don't be vague.
Vicious.
Violent.

Weak.
Weird.
Wicked.

This is the most excellent advice I've ever heard.

II. 短篇英語演講：

Hey guys: 大家好：

Don't undermine others. 不要暗中害人。
Don't **underestimate people.** 不要低估別人。
Don't **be** easily **upset.** 不要容易生氣。

Don't be a **vague** person. 不要做一個說話含糊的人。
Don't engage in **vicious** behavior. 不要做壞事。
Don't be **violent** toward others. 不要對他人粗暴。

Don't be a **weak** person. 不要軟弱。
Don't talk about **weird** things. 不要談論奇怪的事。
Don't have a **wicked** character. 不要有壞的個性。

This is the most excellent advice I've ever heard.
這就我所聽過最棒的建議。

III. 短篇作文：

The Most Excellent Advice I've Ever Heard

Allow me to share the most excellent advice I've ever heard in my life. It goes like this. *For starters, don't undermine* your friends. Don't **underestimate people.** Don't get **upset** and lose your cool. *What's more,* don't make **vague** statements. Don't be a **vicious** person. Don't be a **violent** person. *At the same time,* don't be **weak** and incapable. Don't be a **weird** person. *Most importantly,* avoid **wicked** people.

我所聽過最棒的建議

讓我來分享我一生中聽過最棒的建議。說明如下。首先，不要暗中害朋友。不要低估別人。不要生氣，失去冷靜。此外，不要說不清楚。不要有壞心眼。不要有暴力傾向。同時，不要軟弱無能。不要當怪人。最重要的是，要避開壞人。

　　* cool〔kul〕*n.* 冷靜　　incapable〔ɪn'kepəb!〕*adj.* 無能力的

IV. 填空：

　　First, don't ___1___ yourself by making bad decisions. Don't ___2___ your enemies. Don't be easily ___3___.

　　On the other hand, don't be a ___4___ and obscure person. Don't engage in ___5___ or harmful behavior. Don't be ___6___ toward others.

　　On top of that, don't be a ___7___ person who can't defend himself. Don't talk about ___8___ things. Last but not least, don't have a ___9___ character.

　　首先，不要做不好的決定，損害自己。不要低估你的敵人。不要容易生氣。

　　另一方面，不要做一個說話很含糊的人。不要做壞事。不要對他人粗暴。

　　此外，不要做一個無法保護自己，軟弱的人。不要談論奇怪的事。最後一項要點是，不要有壞的個性。

【解答】 1. undermine　2. underestimate　3. upset
　　　　 4. vague　5. vicious　6. violent　7. weak
　　　　 8. weird　9. wicked
　　　　 * obscure〔əb'skjur〕*adj.* 模糊的
　　　　 engage in 從事　　defend〔dɪ'fɛnd〕*v.* 保護

V. 詞彙題：

Directions: *Choose the one word that best completes the sentence.*

1. Only an evil person tries to _____ a friend.
   (A) undergo　(B) undermine　(C) underline　(D) undertake

2. Your enemies should never be _____.
   (A) uncovered　(B) updated　(C) underestimated　(D) utilized

3. Don't be one of those people who get easily _____ at minor problems.
   (A) upset　(B) upright　(C) utmost　(D) urgent

4. It's hard to be friends with a _____ person.
   (A) valuable　(B) valid　(C) vague　(D) vacant

5. There's nothing less attractive than a person with a _____ temper.
   (A) vertical　(B) verbal　(C) vocal　(D) vicious

6. If you are _____, I'm not coming anywhere near you.
   (A) violent　(B) victorious　(C) versatile　(D) vigorous

7. _____ people are constantly abused and exploited.
   (A) Wary　(B) Weak　(C) Wealthy　(D) Wooden

8. Nobody wants to hang out with a _____ character.
   (A) weird　(B) windy　(C) wonderful　(D) worthy

9. Don't let yourself be deceived by _____ people.
   (A) worthwhile　(B) widespread　(C) wicked　(D) wholesome

【答案】 1.(B)　2.(C)　3.(A)　4.(C)　5.(D)　6.(A)
　　　　 7.(B)　8.(A)　9.(C)

VI. 同義字整理：

1. **undermine** (ˌʌndɚˈmaɪn) *v.* 損害
   - = weaken (ˈwikən)
   - = sabotage (ˈsæbəˌtɑʒ)
   - = damage (ˈdæmɪdʒ)

2. **underestimate** (ˈʌndɚˈɛstəˌmet) *v.* 低估
   - = underrate (ˈʌndɚˌret)
   - = undervalue (ˈʌndɚˈvælju)
   - = belittle (bɪˈlɪtḷ)

3. **upset** (ʌpˈsɛt) *adj.* 不高興的；生氣的
   - = distressed (dɪˈstrɛst)
   - = troubled (ˈtrʌbḷd)
   - = worried (ˈwɝɪd)
   - = unhappy (ʌnˈhæpɪ)

4. **vague** (veg) *adj.* 模糊的
   - = unclear (ʌnˈklɪr)
   - = blurred (blɝd)
   - = obscure (əbˈskjur)
   - = indefinite (ɪnˈdɛfənɪt)
   - = indistinct (ˌɪndɪˈstɪŋkt)

5. **vicious** (ˈvɪʃəs) *adj.* 邪惡的
   - = wicked (ˈwɪkɪd)
   - = malicious (məˈlɪʃəs)
   - = vindictive (vɪnˈdɪktɪv)

6. **violent** (ˈvaɪələnt) *adj.* 暴力的
   - = cruel (ˈkruəl)
   - = brutal (ˈbrutḷ)
   - = savage (ˈsævɪdʒ)
   - = destructive (dɪˈstrʌktɪv)
   - = hot-tempered (ˈhɑtˈtɛmpɚd)

7. **weak** (wik) *adj.* 虛弱的
   - = frail (frel)
   - = feeble (ˈfibḷ)
   - = delicate (ˈdɛləkɪt)
   - = fragile (ˈfrædʒaɪl, ˈfrædʒəl)

8. **weird** (wɪrd) *adj.* 奇怪的
   - = odd (ɑd)
   - = queer (kwɪr)
   - = bizarre (bɪˈzɑr)
   - = strange (strendʒ)

9. **wicked** (ˈwɪkɪd) *adj.* 邪惡的
   - = bad (bæd)
   - = evil (ˈivḷ)
   - = foul (faʊl)
   - = vicious (ˈvɪʃəs)

U

INDEX · 索引

※ 可利用索引，檢查你是否都認識這些字。

索
引

索
引

Good Advice: What Not to Do

全書 216 句

聽「英文一字金」就和聽唸經一樣，再重複不停地唸，就能脫口而出！

1. Don't abandon others.
   Abuse anyone.
   Ambush.

   Argue.
   Assault.
   Assume.

   一回九句，
   可用手機重
   複循環聽。

   Annoy.
   Alienate.
   Be average.

2. Don't beg.
   Betray others.
   Boast.

   Bribe.
   Blame others.
   Break down.

   Don't be brutal.
   Don't be a burden.
   Don't burn your bridges.

3. Don't start conflict.
   Conceal.
   Condemn.

   Cry.
   Curse.
   Criticize.

   Cheat.
   Complain.
   Complicate things.

4. Don't choke.
   Don't get confused.
   Don't be contradictory.

   Cheap.
   Childish.
   Conceited.

   Corrupt.
   Critical.
   Contrary.

5. Don't delay.
   Despair.
   Degrade others.

   Disturb others.
   Distort things.
   Disregard others.

   Discourage others.
   Don't doubt.
   Don't be defeated.

6. Don't be defensive.
   Desperate.
   Destructive.

   Difficult.
   Dishonest.
   Disgraceful.

   Dramatic.
   Dreadful.
   Dreary.

7. Don't exclude others.
Exploit others.
Exaggerate.

Envy others.
Endanger others.
Embarrass others.

Don't be evil.
Extreme.
Emotional.

---

8. Don't fight.
Falter.
Flatter.

Don't be feeble.
Frail.
Fragile.

Forgetful.
Furious.
Frantic.

---

9. Don't fail.
Fear.
Forsake others.

Don't be fake.
False.
Foolish.

Foul.
Frustrated.
A freak.

---

10. Don't groan.
Grumble.
Growl.

Grieve.
Gossip.
Glare.

Don't be greedy.
Grim.
Gloomy.

---

11. Don't hate.
Hurt others.
Hesitate.

Howl.
Harass others.
Humiliate others.

Don't be harsh.
Hasty.
Hysterical.

---

12. Don't invade.
Indulge.
Intrude.

Interfere.
Interrupt.
Intimidate others.

Insult others.
Injure others.
Irritate others.

13. Don't ignore others.
Isolate yourself.
Impose.

Don't be idle.
Ignorant.
Irritable.

Indifferent.
Indignant.
An idiot.

14. Don't judge.
Jeer.
Jaywalk.

Lie.
Litter.
Lament.

Don't be lonely.
Lonesome.
A loser.

15. Don't murmur.
Mutter.
Mumble.

Mock.
Manipulate.
Make a mistake.

Don't be miserable.
Melancholy.
Mournful.

16. Don't be naughty.
Nasty.
Narrow-minded.

Needy.
Nervous.
Nearsighted.

Noisy.
Notorious.
A nuisance.

17. Don't overdo.
Overeat.
Oversleep.

Overwork.
Object.
Offend.

Don't be obscure.
Obstinate.
An obstacle.

18. Don't poke.
Poach.
Postpone.

Preach.
Pretend.
Provoke.

Punch.
Puzzle.
Pirate.

19. Don't refuse.
Refute.
Rebel.

Restrict.
Restrain.
Repress.

Ridicule.
Retaliate.
Seek revenge.

20. Don't be ragged.
Rash.
Reckless.

Rigid.
Ridiculous.
Reluctant.

Rough.
Rotten.
A rascal.

21. Don't scold.
Scorn.
Scream.

Sneer.
Snort.
Snarl.

Don't be shallow.
Shabby.
Sloppy.

22. Don't shout.
Shrug.
Shun others.

Sob.
Stammer.
Stutter.

Swear.
Stumble.
Surrender.

23. Don't tease.
Taunt.
Threaten.

Trip.
Tumble.
Twist.

Don't be tense.
Timid.
Tedious.

24. Don't undermine others.
Underestimate people.
Be upset.

Don't be vague.
Vicious.
Violent.

Weak.
Weird.
Wicked.

顛覆傳統課程

劉毅「英文一字金」每週四上課

　　一個人背單字很辛苦，大家一起背就變簡單。「英文一字金」的發明，將讓同學快速增加單字。寫作能力、會話能力，考試能力都能大幅提升。

Ⅰ. **開課目的：** 把這種顛覆傳統的方法，快速傳播出去，解救受苦受難的同學和老師。背了「英文一字金」，便能看到學好英文的希望。

Ⅱ. **收費標準：** 9,900元（課程結束前，在一分半鐘內背完216句，可得獎學金1萬元）

Ⅲ. **上課內容：** 協助同學背完「英文一字金」216句，並利用這216句排列組合，可以演講、寫作、準備考試。唯有背到一分半鐘之內，變成直覺，成為長期記憶，才能累積。

Ⅳ. **上課時間：** 每週四晚上6:30～9:30，共16週。循環上課，隨到隨上。

Ⅴ. **報名資格：** 不限年齡、不限程度，人人可以參加。特別歡迎英文老師，背完後，把這個革命性的方法傳出去。

Ⅵ. **上課地點：** 台北市許昌街17號6樓　TEL: (02) 2389-5212
　　　　　　　　（台北火車站前，捷運8號出口，1分鐘即可到達）

本書所有人

姓名 ＿＿＿＿＿＿＿＿＿＿＿＿　　電話 ＿＿＿＿＿＿＿＿＿＿

地址 ＿＿＿＿＿＿＿＿＿＿＿＿＿＿＿＿＿＿＿＿＿＿＿＿

（如拾獲本書，請通知本人領取，感激不盡。）

「英文一字金③金玉良言經」背誦記錄表

篇　名	口試通過日　期	口試老師簽　名	篇　名	口試通過日　期	口試老師簽　名
1. A			*13.* I (2)		
2. B			*14.* J , L		
3. C (1)			*15.* M		
4. C (2)			*16.* N		
5. D (1)			*17.* O		
6. D (2)			*18.* P		
7. E			*19.* R (1)		
8. F (1)			*20.* R (2)		
9. F (2)			*21.* S (1)		
10. G			*22.* S (2)		
11. H			*23.* T		
12. I (1)			*24.* U , V , W		

「財團法人臺北市一口氣英語教育基金會」
提供 *100* 萬元獎金，領完為止！

1. 每一回九句，5秒鐘內背完。
2. 每次可背多回，每天口試只限 2 次。
3. 在 1 分半鐘內，背完整本 216 句，可得獎金 2,000 元。
4. 5 分鐘內一次背完「英文一字金①～④」，可再得獎金 2,000 元。
5. 背誦地點：台北市許昌街 17 號 6F–6【一口氣英語教育基金會】
　　TEL: (02) 2389-5212

英文一字金③金玉良言經
One Word English ③ Good Advice:
What Not to Do

售價：280 元

主　　　編／劉　毅

發　行　所／學習出版有限公司　　☎ (02) 2704-5525

郵　撥　帳　號／05127272 學習出版社帳戶

登　記　證／局版台業 2179 號

印　刷　所／裕強彩色印刷有限公司

台　北　門　市／台北市許昌街 10 號 2F　　☎ (02) 2331-4060

台灣總經銷／紅螞蟻圖書有限公司　　☎ (02) 2795-3656

本公司網址　www.learnbook.com.tw

電子郵件　learnbook@learnbook.com.tw

2019 年 5 月 1 日初版

4713269383239

版權所有，本書內容未經書面同意，不得以任何
形式複製。

英文要使用，才不會忘記

有次看到一位美國編輯，愁容滿面，我就跟她說了下面幾句話，她立刻笑了起來。

Don't be miserable.（不要悶悶不樂。）
Don't be melancholy.（不要憂鬱。）
Don't be mournful.（不要哀傷。）

Don't despair.（不要絕望。）
Don't be desperate.（不要絕望。）
Don't be gloomy.（不要悲觀。）

這些單字都在「高中常用7000字」範圍內，同學背了立刻用得到。這些話都是程度高的人說的，一說出來，就讓人佩服。把重要的單字用嘴巴說出來，不會忘記，又能修身養性。

人一定會生氣，脾氣越大，吃虧越大。現在想起來，心驚膽寒，過去說錯了很多話。在「金玉良言經」中有教你：

Don't be defensive.（不要被激怒。）
Don't be dramatic.（不要太激動。）
Don't be dreadful.（不要讓人害怕。）

Don't be furious.（不要生氣。）
Don't be frantic.（不要發狂。）
Don't be irritable.（不要動不動就生氣。）

Don't be upset.（不要不高興。）
Don't be dreary.（不要讓人討厭。）
Don't break down.（不要崩潰。）

嘲笑別人，等於言語霸凌。越是成功、越有錢的人，要更謙虛。我們住家樓下有一位大陸來的清潔人員，小孩小學畢業，為了減輕家裡負擔，要去讀軍校，我送他一萬元獎學金，最受益的是我自己，敬人者，人恆敬之。「金玉良言經」中有：

Don't scorn.（不要輕視人。）
Don't snort.（不要哼鼻子。）
Don't sneer.（不要輕視。）

Don't tease.（不要取笑。）
Don't taunt.（不要嘲笑。）
Don't jeer.（不要嘲笑。）

Don't mock.（不要嘲笑。）
Don't ridicule.（不要嘲笑。）

我在二十幾歲的時候，有一次，有位同事威脅要打我，雖然我當時屈服，但在那以後，我就一直不想見到那個人，他的葬禮我都不想去。所以，我們一定要勸導大家，千萬不要去威脅別人，得逞了，下場更慘。

Don't threaten others.（不要威脅別人。）
Don't intimidate others.（不要威脅別人。）
Don't be rough.（不要粗魯。）

　　近朱者赤，近墨者黑。跟喜歡學英文的人在一起，就會變得喜歡英文。我們有五位語言博士：封四維博士、戴育賢博士、彭維正博士、陳祖昱博士，及吳岳峰博士。大家要把握機會，和他們學習「英文一字金」、當朋友。能夠讀到博士不容易，一定有過人之處。「英文一字金」每天都有課，期待大家參加。英文句子量決定英文的水準，我們不只是在學英文，而是在使用英文。因為使用，無形中就能把英文學好。

劉毅